The
Kew Gardens WORDSEARCH COLLECTION

Royal Botanic Gardens Kew

The Kew Gardens WORDSEARCH COLLECTION

This edition published in 2020 by Arcturus Publishing Limited
26/27 Bickels Yard, 151–153 Bermondsey Street,
London SE1 3HA

AD007957NT

Printed in the UK

1 Individual Trees of Note – Living

Y	L	Z	Z	I	R	G	C	R	O	E	S	T	G	W
J	A	C	R	A	I	G	E	N	D	S	G	N	E	D
O	G	A	R	D	L	E	A	G	E	O	L	A	R	B
G	N	E	N	S	T	Y	L	D	P	L	C	R	N	L
E	O	O	T	O	A	S	I	R	A	V	R	G	I	W
I	I	A	T	K	I	A	T	B	D	H	W	L	K	B
V	R	S	O	L	M	T	N	B	T	R	I	A	A	C
A	U	S	U	O	A	O	A	H	E	G	H	R	K	O
D	T	V	N	N	T	O	I	P	N	N	Y	E	O	M
T	N	D	U	T	L	M	L	A	I	G	N	N	W	F
A	E	L	U	T	M	A	R	A	R	C	J	E	X	O
M	C	B	H	A	J	I	N	A	P	J	N	G	T	R
H	B	N	M	Z	P	A	N	D	O	L	R	A	Y	T
A	A	M	V	X	Z	I	B	A	R	T	E	K	M	P
R	A	O	L	D	T	J	I	K	K	O	A	O	S	E

- ◊ BARTEK
- ◊ BENNETT JUNIPER
- ◊ BUTTONBALL TREE
- ◊ CASHEW OF PIRANGI
- ◊ CENTURION
- ◊ COMFORT MAPLE
- ◊ CRAIGENDS YEW
- ◊ DAVIE POPLAR
- ◊ DIAMOND TREE
- ◊ EL DRAGO
- ◊ EL PALO ALTO
- ◊ EMANCIPATION OAK
- ◊ GENERAL GRANT TREE
- ◊ GERNIKAKO ARBOLA
- ◊ GRANIT OAK
- ◊ GREAT SUGI OF KAYANO
- ◊ GRIZZLY GIANT
- ◊ LUNA
- ◊ OLD TJIKKO
- ◊ PANDO
- ◊ RAHMAT TREE
- ◊ STARA MASLINA
- ◊ SUNLAND BAOBAB
- ◊ THIMMAMMA MARRIMANU

2 Aquatic Plant Species

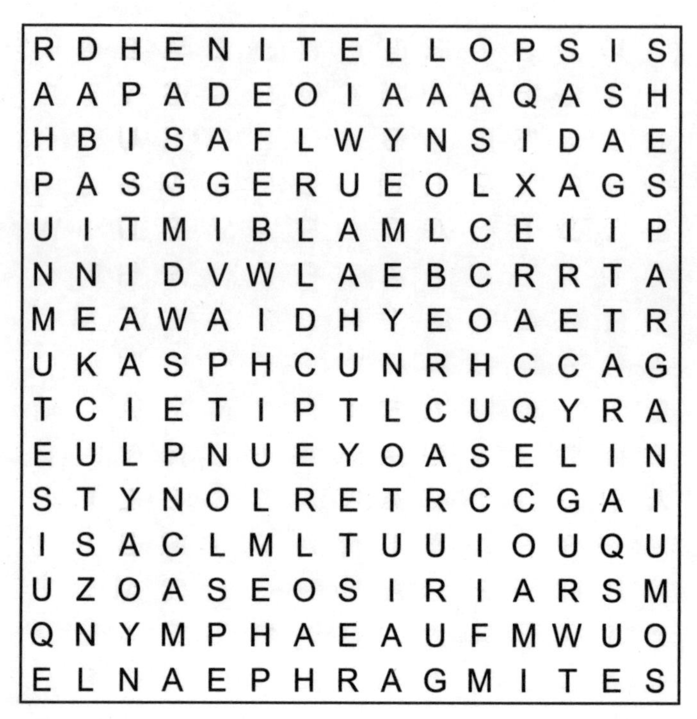

- ◊ *ACORUS*
- ◊ *CAREX*
- ◊ *CENTELLA ASIATICA*
- ◊ *ELEOCHARIS DULCIS*
- ◊ *EQUISETUM FLUVIATILE*
- ◊ *EURYALE FEROX*
- ◊ *GLYCERIA MAXIMA*
- ◊ *IPOMOEA AQUATICA*
- ◊ *IRIS PSEUDACORUS*
- ◊ *LEPILAENA*
- ◊ *LUDWIGIA ADSCENDENS*
- ◊ *NASTURTIUM OFFICINALE*
- ◊ *NELUMBO NUCIFERA*
- ◊ *NITELLOPSIS OBTUSA*
- ◊ *NUPHAR LUTEA*
- ◊ *NYMPHAEA ALBA*
- ◊ *PHRAGMITES AUSTRALIS*
- ◊ *PISTIA*
- ◊ *SAGITTARIA*
- ◊ *SPARGANIUM*
- ◊ *STUCKENIA*
- ◊ *TYPHA*
- ◊ *VICTORIA AMAZONICA*
- ◊ *ZANNICHELLIA*

3

Genera in the Family: Primulaceae (Primrose Family)

A	W	U	S	A	R	E	C	I	G	E	A	E	S	A
I	A	G	F	A	I	H	C	A	M	I	S	Y	L	N
N	L	J	S	L	A	B	I	S	I	A	S	U	B	O
O	L	A	I	Z	E	M	O	E	N	I	M	S	C	A
L	E	D	R	V	G	E	C	B	S	I	B	U	I	L
O	N	F	O	D	A	A	U	E	R	A	R	H	M	B
S	I	A	C	Q	S	L	H	P	D	X	C	T	O	A
A	A	D	N	O	W	T	C	U	T	S	B	N	N	I
E	A	I	R	A	A	R	L	U	T	A	E	A	O	R
P	Y	D	Z	R	G	A	A	O	P	L	S	Y	P	I
E	N	J	A	G	V	A	V	P	L	V	E	L	O	D
A	M	P	E	M	B	E	L	I	A	I	R	B	R	A
A	I	R	E	H	O	L	A	L	A	N	B	M	U	S
F	I	T	T	I	N	G	I	A	I	G	E	A	S	X
E	N	I	S	R	Y	M	V	U	A	S	E	A	M	Y

- ◊ *AEGICERAS*
- ◊ *AMBLYANTHUS*
- ◊ *ANAGALLIS*
- ◊ *ANDROSACE*
- ◊ *BADULA*
- ◊ *BONELLIA*
- ◊ *CLAVIJA*
- ◊ *CORIS*
- ◊ *EMBELIA*
- ◊ *FITTINGIA*
- ◊ *LABISIA*
- ◊ *LOHERIA*
- ◊ *LYSIMACHIA*
- ◊ *MAESA*
- ◊ *MONOPORUS*
- ◊ *MYRSINE*
- ◊ *NEOMEZIA*
- ◊ *PARATHESIS*
- ◊ *PRIMULA*
- ◊ *RAPANEA*
- ◊ *SADIRIA*
- ◊ *SOLONIA*
- ◊ *VOTSCHIA*
- ◊ *WALLENIA*

4 Roses (Common Names)

I	R	O	C	K	A	N	D	R	O	L	L	A	E	L
L	O	V	E	L	Y	F	A	I	R	Y	D	I	E	A
W	U	C	B	A	R	E	C	A	F	L	E	G	N	A
S	P	A	F	C	N	A	J	N	G	H	S	L	A	O
G	E	S	L	A	S	I	I	H	L	N	D	A	L	G
N	N	I	E	A	I	N	R	D	C	W	E	T	Y	Y
I	I	N	R	M	L	R	E	E	H	I	M	S	N	H
S	W	O	I	A	O	H	B	D	L	D	O	O	N	S
S	R	I	F	L	S	O	O	I	R	L	N	N	E	I
E	E	C	D	I	Y	E	N	O	A	A	A	L	P	R
L	M	E	L	B	L	M	D	D	P	N	G	B	J	E
B	M	B	I	A	V	N	M	E	A	G	C	W	E	H
O	U	E	W	B	I	N	A	C	I	N	F	A	E	C
T	S	R	F	A	A	C	S	G	A	K	C	R	S	K
O	I	G	S	A	E	S	L	A	R	O	C	E	O	K

◊ AGNES
◊ ALBA
◊ ALIBABA
◊ ANGEL FACE
◊ BALLERINA
◊ BLESSINGS
◊ CASINO
◊ CHERISH
◊ CORAL SEAS
◊ DESDEMONA
◊ FAIR BIANCA
◊ GIGGLES
◊ ICEBERG
◊ KEW GARDENS
◊ LOVELY FAIRY
◊ MOONDANCE
◊ NOSTALGIA
◊ OOH LA LA
◊ PEACE
◊ PENNY LANE
◊ ROCK AND ROLL
◊ SUMMER WINE
◊ SYLVIA
◊ WILD FIRE

5 Famous Botanists – Part One

U	J	A	R	V	E	R	A	S	T	I	N	G	A	L
F	A	P	A	H	Y	M	A	L	L	E	B	L	D	E
F	M	S	T	E	L	L	E	R	I	U	R	I	A	D
B	A	F	E	D	O	U	G	L	A	S	O	N	A	N
A	H	E	R	L	Y	R	D	A	B	R	W	N	R	E
N	T	V	O	M	A	N	G	O	N	T	N	A	B	M
K	N	A	N	E	F	M	E	E	M	X	T	E	E	A
S	E	S	I	K	V	R	M	V	S	I	R	U	R	L
V	B	T	P	N	H	O	E	A	A	S	R	S	P	D
S	B	G	L	A	A	T	L	B	D	R	N	M	E	S
T	F	S	A	B	Z	I	L	I	S	T	A	E	N	M
O	O	V	S	R	A	A	T	E	V	S	U	I	R	I
P	E	R	E	U	L	N	E	O	S	A	K	C	Q	T
E	A	A	C	B	E	R	A	O	N	T	V	W	G	H
S	D	Y	Y	T	P	B	N	T	A	T	H	E	O	S

◊ WILLIAM AITON
◊ IBN AL-BAITAR
◊ JANAKI AMMAL
◊ AGNES ARBER
◊ ANNA ATKINS
◊ JOSEPH BANKS
◊ DAVID BELLAMY
◊ GEORGE BENTHAM
◊ HERMAN BOERHAAVE
◊ ROBERT BROWN
◊ LUTHER BURBANK
◊ ANDREA CESALPINO
◊ DAVID DOUGLAS
◊ KATHERINE ESAU
◊ CONRAD GESSNER
◊ CARL LINNAEUS
◊ FRANCIS MASSON
◊ GREGOR MENDEL
◊ PETER H. RAVEN
◊ JOHN RAY
◊ JAMES EDWARD SMITH
◊ GEORG WILHELM STELLER
◊ MARIE STOPES
◊ NIKOLAI VAVILOV

6 William Wordsworth – *I Wandered Lonely as a Cloud* (1807)

I wandered lonely as a cloud
That floats on high o'er vales and hills,
When all at once I saw a crowd,
A host, of golden daffodils;
Beside the lake, beneath the trees,
Fluttering and dancing in the breeze.

Continuous as the stars that shine
And twinkle on the milky way,
They stretched in never-ending line
Along the margin of a bay:
Ten thousand saw I at a glance,
Tossing their heads in sprightly dance.

The waves beside them danced; but they
Out-did the sparkling waves in glee:
A poet could not but be gay,
In such a jocund company:
I gazed—and gazed—but little thought
What wealth the show to me had brought:

For oft, when on my couch I lie
In vacant or in pensive mood,
They flash upon that inward eye
Which is the bliss of solitude;
And then my heart with pleasure fills,
And dances with the daffodils.

D	E	H	C	T	E	R	T	S	L	A	K	E	D	H
M	S	F	L	O	A	T	S	C	N	F	B	W	E	G
Y	P	H	T	A	E	N	E	B	P	R	O	D	E	I
C	R	A	I	F	L	U	T	T	E	R	I	N	G	H
N	I	G	R	A	M	R	W	E	C	S	E	O	T	E
T	G	C	M	H	E	I	Z	O	E	V	L	O	C	D
R	H	I	I	I	N	E	N	B	E	D	S	N	W	N
E	T	L	D	K	L	T	D	R	E	S	A	A	S	A
E	L	M	L	A	I	K	E	N	I	L	N	Z	D	S
S	Y	E	V	N	N	N	Y	N	G	D	B	L	A	U
T	V	T	U	A	D	C	G	P	E	U	A	O	E	O
A	L	O	S	I	L	E	I	R	O	P	Y	N	H	H
R	U	R	N	O	A	E	E	N	I	H	S	E	C	T
S	U	G	U	I	H	D	S	J	G	N	O	L	A	E
R	E	D	A	F	F	O	D	I	L	S	A	Y	M	T

7

Botanical Artists and Illustrators – Part One

G D A L B Y S A T D E E S D N

A D R S A M E A R D X E E A R

R R A A I R N A G E L S E M K

Z E W T K I R I I L H D R O A

O S H Y K E H T A A H R H U N

N P U B V Y O R R N C A E E D

I C M E H A S O C Y T W Y T E

J A X C H H B E S G I D G R L

L Q L Y E T R W S N F E T S R

L T E A C W R B O I E H W G E

S I T U H T E O R L H B B B U

H P T A U S F N N L C R O E A

A X Y V R H R E E E I L O T B

U M T H C P N A S N U Z T T A

Y H E L H W R O M S E T H E P

◊ FERDINAND BAUER
◊ HARRY BOLUS
◊ RAYMOND BOOTH
◊ ARTHUR HARRY CHURCH
◊ CLAIRE DALBY
◊ MARY DELANY
◊ SARAH DRAKE
◊ SYDENHAM EDWARDS
◊ GEORG DIONYSIUS EHRET
◊ BARBARA EVERARD
◊ WALTER HOOD FITCH
◊ GIOVANNA GARZONI
◊ DAVID KANDEL
◊ DEBORAH LAMBKIN
◊ CYTHNA LETTY
◊ ALEXANDER MARSHAL
◊ RORY MCEWEN
◊ MARGARET MEE
◊ MARIANNE NORTH
◊ ANNE PRATT
◊ STELLA ROSS-CRAIG
◊ PANDORA SELLARS
◊ MATILDA SMITH
◊ LILIAN SNELLING

8 Recent Discoveries – 2016 onwards

```
I H A I N A M I N A M I H C U
I U B C L A B A M B U S A E O
K R B E B L G N T X A I R A H
E T U R R O P N A O X L O E L
E E R G D C E M A M V I L N S
H R S I B I I A Y G B B F M P
C I A O B T A L I I L A I E I
I V N F A R N R I R I R D L I
F I U E R E A N E A A I N I T
I T S Y B S W C D F E M A T E
A T I I A E D R T L I T R O D
I A B N T D S I V E A L G S A
R T I N A C C E S S A F O A C
L A A D O L I N A E C T C R E
E R K O R U P E N S I S A X P
```

◊ *BARLERIA DESERTICOLA*

◊ *BARLERIA MIRABILIS*

◊ *BARLERIA NAMBA*

◊ *BULBOPHYLLUM ADOLINAE*

◊ *COSTULARIA CADETII*

◊ *CYRTANDRA VITTATA*

◊ *DIOSCOREA HURTERI*

◊ *GALANTHUS BURSANUS*

◊ *GAMBEYA KORUPENSIS*

◊ *GLADIOLUS MARIAE*

◊ *HOHENBUEHELIA BONII*

◊ *HYDNUM MELITOSARX*

◊ *IPOMOEA INACCESSA*

◊ *IPOMOEA PROLIFERA*

◊ *KINDIA GANGAN*

◊ *LEBBIEA GRANDIFLORA*

◊ *LEMUROPHOENIX LAEVIS*

◊ *NEPENTHES BIAK*

◊ *OREOCHARIS TRIBRACTEATA*

◊ *PIMENTA BERCILIAE*

◊ *RUBROSHIRAIA BAMBUSAE*

◊ *SEYCHELLARIA BARBATA*

◊ *SYNSEPALUM CHIMANIMANI*

◊ *TALBOTIELLA CHEEKII*

9 Genera in the Family: Rosaceae – Part One (Rose Family)

A	I	N	I	T	O	H	P	S	U	R	Y	P	H	S
F	A	B	R	O	S	I	U	G	N	A	S	S	U	F
S	O	R	B	A	R	O	N	I	A	T	H	B	O	A
U	P	O	P	A	C	A	S	I	B	I	R	A	E	A
T	A	I	U	G	C	I	I	Y	A	O	A	S	M	I
A	I	T	R	Y	V	A	N	L	S	O	I	E	L	O
B	G	Y	S	A	C	I	I	D	E	L	E	A	E	A
O	N	L	H	Z	E	R	I	N	Y	K	I	N	R	I
N	A	O	I	T	D	A	A	T	E	N	R	C	I	R
A	H	S	A	S	A	O	S	T	E	M	D	O	A	A
L	I	P	R	I	U	A	C	D	A	R	R	M	H	M
E	A	E	R	S	M	L	D	Y	Y	E	E	A	Z	L
M	T	R	I	O	P	A	A	A	N	N	G	R	E	U
A	E	M	C	Y	M	W	S	M	R	I	U	U	S	H
K	P	A	R	U	N	C	U	S	N	I	A	M	S	E

- ◊ *ACOMASTYLIS*
- ◊ *ARMENIACA*
- ◊ *ARUNCUS*
- ◊ *COMARUM*
- ◊ *CRATAEGUS*
- ◊ *DOCYNIA*
- ◊ *DRYAS*
- ◊ *HORKELIA*
- ◊ *KERRIA*
- ◊ *MADDENIA*
- ◊ *MALUS*
- ◊ *MELANOBATUS*
- ◊ *OEMLERIA*
- ◊ *PHOTINIA*
- ◊ *PURSHIA*
- ◊ *PYRUS*
- ◊ *SANGUISORBA*
- ◊ *SIBIRAEA*
- ◊ *SORBARONIA*
- ◊ *SORBUS*
- ◊ *SPIRAEA*
- ◊ *TAIHANGIA*
- ◊ *TYLOSPERMA*
- ◊ *ULMARIA*

10 Collections at Kew

- ◊ ALPINE AND ROCK GARDEN
- ◊ AQUATIC COLLECTION
- ◊ ARBORETUM
- ◊ ARID COLLECTION
- ◊ AROID COLLECTION
- ◊ BONSAI COLLECTION
- ◊ BROMELIAD COLLECTION
- ◊ CARNIVOROUS PLANT COLLECTION
- ◊ CYCAD COLLECTION
- ◊ ECONOMIC BOTANY COLLECTION
- ◊ FERN COLLECTION
- ◊ GRASS COLLECTION
- ◊ IN VITRO COLLECTION
- ◊ ISLAND FLORA COLLECTION
- ◊ MICROSCOPE SLIDE COLLECTION
- ◊ ORCHID COLLECTION
- ◊ PALM COLLECTION
- ◊ SEED COLLECTION
- ◊ SPIRIT COLLECTION
- ◊ TENDER TEMPERATE COLLECTION
- ◊ THE ARCHIVES COLLECTION
- ◊ THE FUNGARIUM
- ◊ THE HERBARIUM
- ◊ THE LIBRARY

11

Genera in the Family: Orchidaceae – Part One (Orchid Family)

```
A S S O L G O S S O R C E R O
P P L A T Y R H I Z A Q U S A
S I T T O L G O C O L P N I L
B A I R A L U P I T A T R X Z
A C U A I Q U J O M I A S E E
I A J V L S U G E V N M I L L
S T R D E S U D N N O C R P E
O T M Y O T I L E A S A A O N
T L U V C N R G I A A L E M K
O E P A P U A E A H K O L Y O
P Y I S N D P B A Y C P A D A
F A B D O M I N E A I O G I F
S I N C Y C Y L O P D G C D C
T R O P I D I A G A R O S S F
S U T S A L B I P E V N P Q A
```

◊ *ABDOMINEA*

◊ *ANGULOA*

◊ *ASCOCHILUS*

◊ *CALOPOGON*

◊ *CATTLEYA*

◊ *COELIA*

◊ *CROSSOGLOSSA*

◊ *DICKASONIA*

◊ *DIDYMOPLEXIS*

◊ *EPIBLASTUS*

◊ *GALEARIS*

◊ *GENNARIA*

◊ *NIDEMA*

◊ *PAPUAEA*

◊ *PLATYRHIZA*

◊ *PLOCOGLOTTIS*

◊ *POLYCYCNIS*

◊ *POTOSIA*

◊ *SAUVETREA*

◊ *TIPULARIA*

◊ *TROPIDIA*

◊ *ZELENKOA*

12 Genera in the Family: Asteraceae – Part One (Daisy Family)

B	O	C	A	R	P	H	O	C	H	A	E	T	E	F
A	R	A	P	O	T	O	S	P	E	R	M	U	M	U
G	E	I	A	M	B	M	F	U	N	G	A	R	N	F
S	H	X	D	M	Z	R	Z	A	E	S	S	E	J	A
P	C	Y	A	X	U	H	E	U	H	S	E	A	P	A
H	I	Z	E	M	L	I	M	B	A	R	D	A	A	I
I	R	Y	D	V	O	U	B	N	M	P	E	L	R	L
L	T	Z	T	Z	H	C	T	O	E	A	I	S	A	U
A	I	V	E	T	S	O	O	T	R	H	A	I	G	E
C	P	A	S	E	S	H	A	R	P	T	L	B	Y	R
T	E	E	F	I	G	L	D	O	E	U	E	E	N	V
I	D	N	A	Z	A	R	C	A	L	T	I	P	O	E
S	M	U	S	C	H	L	E	R	I	A	E	A	X	H
U	S	I	T	C	A	N	E	A	H	C	O	H	Y	C
E	N	E	O	J	E	F	F	R	E	Y	A	D	S	X

◊ *AMBERBOA*

◊ *CARPHOCHAETE*

◊ *CHAENACTIS*

◊ *CHEVREULIA*

◊ *EPITRICHE*

◊ *HETEROCOMA*

◊ *JALCOPHILA*

◊ *JESSEA*

◊ *LIMBARDA*

◊ *LULIA*

◊ *MUSCHLERIA*

◊ *NEOJEFFREYA*

◊ *OTOSPERMUM*

◊ *PARAGYNOXYS*

◊ *PETALACTE*

◊ *PETROBIUM*

◊ *PHILACTIS*

◊ *SANTOSIA*

◊ *STEVIA*

◊ *ZYZYXIA*

13 Coniferous Trees (Common Names)

- ◊ ALPINE JUNIPER
- ◊ ATLAS CEDAR
- ◊ BALSAM FIR
- ◊ CAROLINA HEMLOCK
- ◊ CATKIN YEW
- ◊ COAST REDWOOD
- ◊ CORKBARK FIR
- ◊ CYPRUS CEDAR
- ◊ DOUGLAS FIR
- ◊ EZO SPRUCE
- ◊ FLORIN YEW
- ◊ GIANT SEQUOIA
- ◊ KAURI
- ◊ KHASI PINE
- ◊ MASTERS LARCH
- ◊ MEKONG JUNIPER
- ◊ POND PINE
- ◊ RED SPRUCE
- ◊ SITKA SPRUCE
- ◊ STONE PINE
- ◊ SWISS PINE
- ◊ TAMARACK
- ◊ TORREY PINE
- ◊ WULU PINE

14 IUCN Red List Critically Endangered – Part One (Common Names)

I N D A S S N A I S R A K E U
P A V A N B A Y T O P S J H G
A Y L O A W O L L E M I A Q M
B T R X I N T P J I A O N V S
A E V V L S N A R R U C P Y B
H S O O I K O K I A U A K R P
U H A E C Y U E V S C W Q N O
S O H B I S U C N I H P U A K
R E A A S T O E F T U V A I E
E R G I H A T I B T L U D I M
N A I P S A C L S J H R C A E
G N M T C Q S U E I D A S W B
A J A E I O H E H Y W E S A O
W L I S E K B E A T S P A H Y
T C A H S I F Y L L E J A R A

◊ ATLAS CYPRESS
◊ BARN FERN
◊ BAYTOP'S ONION
◊ CASPIAN KNOTWEED
◊ COASTAL IRIS
◊ CURRAN'S PITOGO
◊ HAHA
◊ HAWAIIAN VETCH
◊ HERON'S BILL
◊ IDA'S SALSIFY
◊ JELLYFISH TREE
◊ KARSIAN CHERVIL
◊ KAUAI KOKI'O
◊ KHUSTUP CAMPION
◊ LEY'S WHITEBEAM
◊ OAHU CHEWSTICK
◊ PACIFIC LACEFERN
◊ PEAR CLERMONTIA
◊ POKEMEBOY
◊ SEA MARIGOLD
◊ SICILIAN FIR
◊ SPINY LOGWOOD
◊ WAGNERS' CORDIA
◊ WOLLEMI PINE

15 National Flowers (Common Names)

- ◊ ARABIAN JASMINE (INDONESIA)
- ◊ BEAR'S BREECH (GREECE)
- ◊ BLUE POPPY (BHUTAN)
- ◊ BLUE-EYED GRASS (BERMUDA)
- ◊ CEIBO (ARGENTINA)
- ◊ CHRISTMAS ORCHID (COLOMBIA)
- ◊ COPIHUE (CHILE)
- ◊ DAGGER'S LOG (ANTIGUA AND BARBUDA)
- ◊ EDELWEISS (SWITZERLAND/AUSTRIA)
- ◊ HEILALA (TONGA)
- ◊ IRIS (FRANCE)
- ◊ KANTUTA (BOLIVIA)
- ◊ KING PROTEA (SOUTH AFRICA)
- ◊ KOWHAI (NEW ZEALAND)
- ◊ LOTUS (INDIA)
- ◊ PINK ROSE (MALDIVES)
- ◊ PLUM BLOSSOM (CHINA)
- ◊ RED GINGER (SAMOA)
- ◊ RED POPPY (BELGIUM)
- ◊ RHODODENDRON (NEPAL)
- ◊ RUMDUOL (CAMBODIA)
- ◊ TULIP (NETHERLANDS)
- ◊ WATER LILY (BANGLADESH)
- ◊ YELLOW ELDER (BAHAMAS)

16 Botanical Terms – Part One

U	D	M	Y	I	H	L	H	E	G	B	C	L	H	E
J	T	R	I	S	S	Z	A	M	M	I	B	P	L	P
R	E	T	E	D	D	I	F	T	M	A	J	O	S	E
A	T	F	N	U	R	E	S	G	S	N	B	A	N	R
H	A	R	E	A	Q	I	E	E	E	I	R	A	E	I
E	L	M	R	U	T	T	B	T	H	R	D	F	C	T
F	U	E	Y	E	I	I	P	Z	A	T	B	F	T	N
T	C	F	P	N	D	E	U	L	C	V	N	O	A	E
U	I	L	U	U	D	C	U	Q	A	O	A	A	R	E
S	T	O	A	I	R	C	C	E	E	R	A	L	A	R
S	E	L	C	S	I	D	T	R	A	D	T	T	C	G
O	R	E	M	T	S	A	Z	H	L	I	R	N	B	R
C	L	T	N	V	L	S	T	E	O	R	N	U	E	E
K	P	E	T	A	G	U	J	E	B	R	R	R	S	V
Q	L	G	T	I	B	A	H	A	D	R	N	A	N	E

- ◊ ALATE
- ◊ ANTHESIS
- ◊ BOLE
- ◊ BURR
- ◊ CLASS
- ◊ CLAVATE
- ◊ DISTAL
- ◊ DRUPE
- ◊ DRUSE
- ◊ ENTIRE
- ◊ EQUITANT
- ◊ EVERGREEN
- ◊ HABIT
- ◊ JUGATE
- ◊ LENTICULAR
- ◊ MIDRIB
- ◊ NECTAR
- ◊ PEDICEL
- ◊ PYRENE
- ◊ RETICULATE
- ◊ THORN
- ◊ TUSSOCK
- ◊ UNITEGMIC
- ◊ VENTRAL

17 Carnivorous Plants (Common Names)

C	B	W	D	E	P	M	U	H	P	E	P	F	E	S
O	E	A	A	P	O	D	E	A	A	A	E	P	U	W
M	C	N	C	T	E	C	R	F	R	O	I	N	E	P
M	S	E	Y	N	E	R	O	T	U	N	E	R	P	A
O	W	S	I	W	O	R	S	G	K	V	C	Q	B	D
N	O	P	E	T	K	Y	W	P	O	S	Z	E	D	E
H	L	H	H	E	R	X	E	H	K	R	A	H	W	L
A	L	M	D	E	M	T	D	R	E	K	G	G	O	D
T	E	D	D	O	T	C	O	A	E	E	U	O	B	D
A	Y	W	D	I	E	C	R	D	E	S	L	Z	N	A
W	O	E	C	C	F	M	O	N	K	E	Y	M	I	S
P	S	O	I	G	A	A	Y	Y	N	A	B	L	A	E
T	A	L	S	U	R	P	I	C	O	B	R	A	R	D
T	A	P	U	R	P	L	E	R	C	D	A	S	V	I
B	L	U	E	C	O	A	T	S	Y	G	E	N	R	S

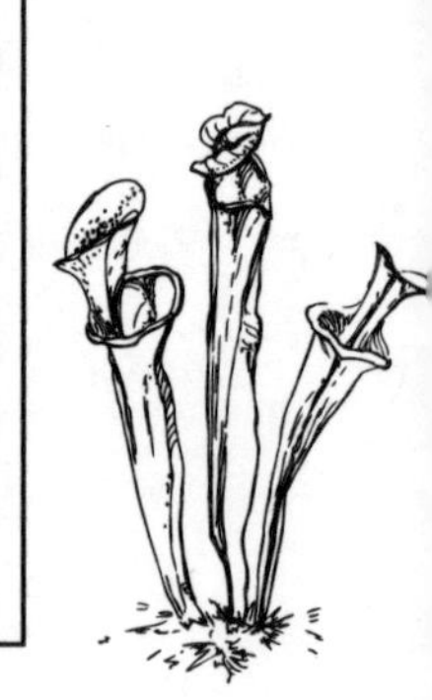

◊ ALBANY PITCHER PLANT
◊ ALICE SUNDEW
◊ ALPINE BUTTERWORT
◊ BEAKED TRIGGERPLANT
◊ BLUECOATS
◊ CAPE SUNDEW
◊ COBRA LILY
◊ COMMON BUTTERWORT
◊ CORKSCREW PLANT
◊ FAIRY APRONS
◊ FORKED SUNDEW
◊ GORGONS DEWSTICK
◊ HUMPED BLADDERWORT
◊ MODEST RAINBOW
◊ MONKEY CUPS
◊ PARROT PITCHER PLANT
◊ PINK PETTICOAT
◊ POWDERY STRAP AIRPLANT
◊ PURPLE TRUMPET-LEAF
◊ RAINBOW PLANT
◊ SIDE-SADDLE FLOWER
◊ VENUS FLYTRAP
◊ WATERWHEEL PLANT
◊ YELLOW TRUMPET

18

Fictional Plants, Trees and Plant-Like Creatures

```
L D E V I T R I F F I D S F L
O R S Y N P N D O O W R I E W
N A I K K E L A R G E T N I H
G E S C V G K D E B R O C L O
A B I O I R R A T R N F I B M
R E B L N A E O R R T F S L P
N E O T E G D D O D A A F A I
I R W H T S B L W T N D N C N
P T T G W R L E R E L A I K G
H X R I V A U E L Y E B M M W
R B U N M T E F Z L S D L E I
E M C X E T I N F E A Y O R L
D D K S M A G E B U L B T C L
I Y L D I O N Y R K L A H Y O
L A E N I R N R O O T A C E W
```

◊ BLACK MERCY
◊ BOWTRUCKLE
◊ BROC FLOWER
◊ GROOT
◊ INKVINE
◊ INTEGRAL TREES
◊ KRYNOID
◊ LIFA TREE
◊ MAGEBULB SEED
◊ MALLORN
◊ MANDRAKE
◊ NIGHTLOCK
◊ NIMLOTH
◊ NIPHREDIL
◊ NIRNROOT
◊ RED WEED
◊ SONGBELL SEED
◊ TESLA TREES
◊ TREANT
◊ TREEBEARD
◊ TRIFFIDS
◊ TRUFFULA TREE
◊ WEIRWOOD
◊ WHOMPING WILLOW

19 IUCN Red List Extinct Plants and Trees

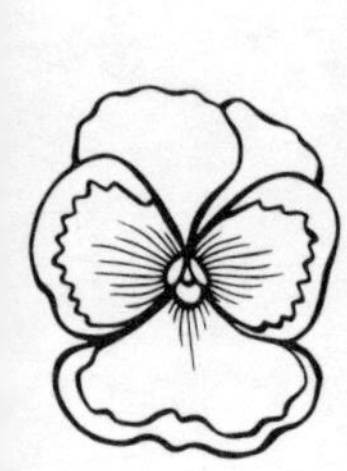

- ◊ ACALYPHA RUBRINERVIS
- ◊ ACHYRANTHES ATOLLENSIS
- ◊ ADIANTUM LIANXIANENSE
- ◊ BLUTAPARON RIGIDUM
- ◊ BYTTNERIA IVORENSIS
- ◊ CAMPOMANESIA LUNDIANA
- ◊ CASEARIA TINIFOLIA
- ◊ CRUDIA ZEYLANICA
- ◊ CYNOMETRA BEDDOMEI
- ◊ GUETTARDA RETUSA
- ◊ HOPEA SHINGKENG
- ◊ ILEX GARDNERIANA
- ◊ KOKIA LANCEOLATA
- ◊ LICANIA CALDASIANA
- ◊ MELICOPE HALEAKALAE
- ◊ MYRCIA SKELDINGII
- ◊ NESIOTA ELLIPTICA
- ◊ OCHROSIA TAHITENSIS
- ◊ ORBEXILUM STIPULATUM
- ◊ POUTERIA STENOPHYLLA
- ◊ PRADOSIA ARGENTEA
- ◊ PSIADIA SCHWEINFURTHII
- ◊ SPOROBOLUS DURUS
- ◊ VIOLA CRYANA

20 Plants of the Rocky Mountains

◊ *ACER GLABRUM*
◊ *ALLIUM GEYERI*
◊ *ASTER ALPINUS*
◊ *BERLANDIERA LYRATE*
◊ *CALYPSO BULBOSA*
◊ *CREPIS ATRIBARBA*
◊ *DASIPHORA FRUTICOSA*
◊ *DRABA GLOBOSA*
◊ *GAILLARDIA ARISTATA*
◊ *LARIX LYALLII*
◊ *NEOTTIA BOREALIS*
◊ *OPUNTIA FRAGILIS*
◊ *PACKERA CANA*
◊ *PANICUM VIRGATUM*
◊ *PENSTEMON ROSTRIFLORUS*
◊ *PICEA GLAUCA*
◊ *QUERCUS GAMBELII*
◊ *RHODIOLA ROSEA*
◊ *RIBES MONTIGENUM*
◊ *ROSA WOODSII*
◊ *SALIX EXIGUA*
◊ *SILENE SCOULERI*
◊ *THUJA PLICATA*
◊ *YUCCA GLAUCA*

21 Desert Flora (Common Names)

A N C D O O W N O R I D W N R
I A R A E E U A O A R W O A E
N F E P A N E L R O A E L F N
R E O E M I V C R O P C L E R
O S S F S E H A A Y N S E T O
F O O S L I U C H L L D Y A H
I A T V V G H L S O Q I Y D T
L P E L A P M L L T N U L H E
A T C S F B E A R A I E A L K
C R P M H R F I R Y B W Y T O
B E S O R G A N P I P E L A M
A E L A S N H C P Y G S S E S
C L B Z G N I P M U J O A A W
Y B O L N A U H S O J S L G B
E F E N I T N E P R U T E D H

- ◊ BARREL CACTUS
- ◊ BASEBALL PLANT
- ◊ CALIFORNIA JUNIPER
- ◊ CREOSOTE BUSH
- ◊ DATE FAN PALM
- ◊ DESERT HOLLY
- ◊ DESERT IRONWOOD
- ◊ DESERT LILY
- ◊ DESERT MARIGOLD
- ◊ DESERT SPOON
- ◊ HONEY MESQUITE
- ◊ HYDNORA AFRICANA
- ◊ JOSHUA TREE
- ◊ JUMPING CHOLLA
- ◊ LACE CACTUS
- ◊ ORGAN PIPE CACTUS
- ◊ SAGUARO CACTUS
- ◊ SMOKETHORN
- ◊ SOAPTREE YUCCA
- ◊ TRIANGLE BURSAGE
- ◊ TURPENTINE BROOM
- ◊ VELVET MESQUITE
- ◊ WELWITSCHIA MIRABILIS
- ◊ YELLOW PALOVERDE

22 Plant Families Beginning with A

E	E	E	A	N	N	O	N	A	C	E	A	E	Z	E
A	A	S	A	E	E	A	E	C	A	R	U	E	N	A
E	E	A	T	E	H	A	A	E	C	R	A	A	L	E
C	C	P	A	S	C	E	C	H	B	A	N	E	A	C
A	A	E	A	E	C	A	I	P	A	A	A	C	R	A
H	I	G	I	M	N	D	O	A	L	E	R	A	A	T
T	O	A	G	Y	I	N	R	Z	C	Z	T	R	L	N
N	L	A	C	A	W	E	A	A	I	J	H	O	I	A
A	H	O	C	H	C	T	R	G	H	A	R	C	A	I
C	P	E	Z	A	E	A	A	H	A	W	I	A	C	D
A	A	A	C	A	D	O	X	A	C	E	A	E	E	A
E	X	E	C	A	S	T	E	L	I	A	C	E	A	E
A	A	E	X	T	O	X	I	C	A	C	E	A	E	O
E	A	E	C	A	G	A	R	A	P	S	A	D	A	G
E	A	D	E	L	A	N	T	H	A	C	E	A	E	A

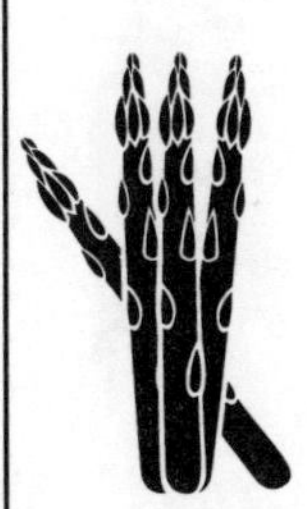

◊ *ACANTHACEAE*

◊ *ACORACEAE*

◊ *ADELANTHACEAE*

◊ *ADIANTACEAE*

◊ *ADOXACEAE*

◊ *AEXTOXICACEAE*

◊ *AIZOACEAE*

◊ *ALZATEACEAE*

◊ *ANARTHRIACEAE*

◊ *ANEURACEAE*

◊ *ANNONACEAE*

◊ *APHLOIACEAE*

◊ *APIACEAE*

◊ *APOCYNACEAE*

◊ *ARACEAE*

◊ *ARALIACEAE*

◊ *ARCHIDIACEAE*

◊ *ARECACEAE*

◊ *ASPARAGACEAE*

◊ *ASTELIACEAE*

23 Moss Genera – Part One

B	M	S	C	I	A	R	O	M	I	O	P	S	I	S
E	U	S	C	H	I	S	T	I	D	I	U	M	E	N
D	I	P	B	S	M	M	K	I	A	E	R	I	A	A
A	N	D	R	J	A	B	U	X	B	A	U	M	I	A
I	M	E	J	O	R	P	S	I	T	Z	U	G	H	I
M	O	V	N	Y	T	Z	A	S	D	N	N	T	C	L
M	C	A	U	C	R	O	P	E	P	I	E	V	U	E
I	A	M	I	C	A	X	S	Y	T	T	U	T	R	T
R	L	F	V	K	B	L	H	P	R	I	Z	H	B	U
G	U	V	U	V	A	O	Y	A	H	Y	M	D	T	E
N	A	O	N	N	R	K	P	P	G	A	N	M	E	R
E	A	N	G	G	A	H	A	O	T	Z	G	V	I	B
S	F	M	Y	R	I	R	D	T	A	A	G	N	P	A
I	C	H	S	S	O	O	I	O	P	E	T	E	U	R
S	O	R	R	Q	N	A	E	A	H	P	Y	R	C	M

◊ *AULACOMNIUM*

◊ *BARTRAMIA*

◊ *BREUTELIA*

◊ *BRUCHIA*

◊ *BRYUM*

◊ *BUXBAUMIA*

◊ *CRYPHAEA*

◊ *ENCALYPTA*

◊ *FUNARIA*

◊ *GRIMMIA*

◊ *HYGROHYPNUM*

◊ *KIAERIA*

◊ *PROTOSPHAGNUM*

◊ *SCHISTIDIUM*

◊ *SCIAROMIOPSIS*

◊ *TAKAKIA*

◊ *TETRAPHIS*

◊ *THUIDIUM*

◊ *TIMMIA*

◊ *ZYGODON*

Excerpt – *Kew Gardens* (1908)
by A. R. Hope Moncrieff

T	H	O	R	O	U	G	H	L	Y	S	W	E	K	O
A	F	E	X	O	T	I	C	D	E	M	H	L	S	R
R	P	A	R	I	S	H	G	E	D	R	O	A	E	I
O	O	H	Y	A	K	N	E	S	A	O	S	N	M	G
U	I	G	I	V	I	N	G	R	D	F	E	O	A	I
N	N	O	L	D	C	N	T	U	O	N	I	I	H	N
D	T	E	N	H	O	O	H	N	G	F	R	T	T	A
E	S	I	I	M	W	F	C	L	A	S	O	A	Q	L
S	W	N	A	E	L	D	I	H	P	R	M	N	U	N
S	A	A	R	A	K	S	H	H	C	A	E	R	A	E
E	W	I	T	S	H	A	W	Q	U	E	M	E	I	T
U	N	H	N	E	E	G	I	L	U	B	A	W	N	T
G	B	E	E	N	R	E	U	H	I	A	N	O	T	I
S	E	V	O	R	G	E	M	O	O	O	Y	H	E	R
S	T	W	I	N	E	D	D	S	H	T	S	O	M	W

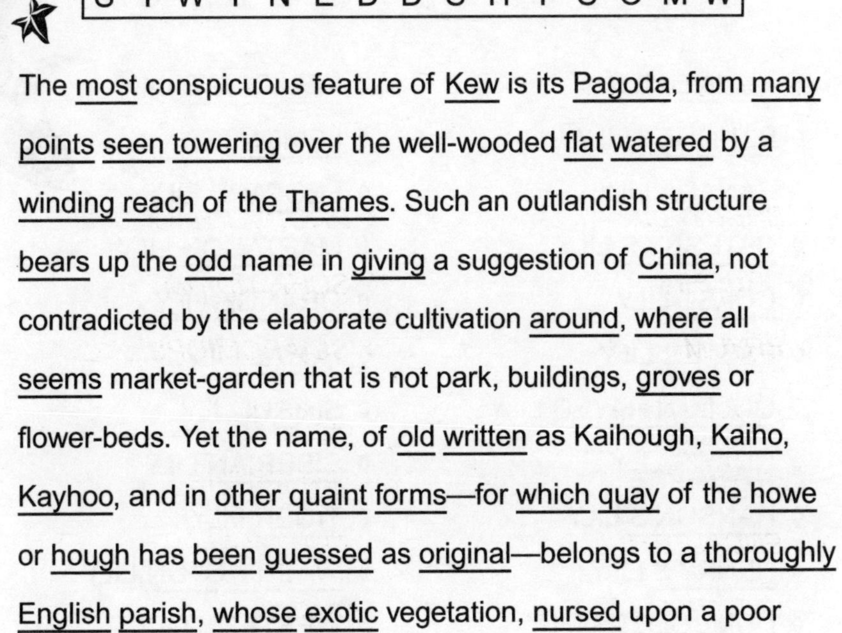

The most conspicuous feature of Kew is its Pagoda, from many points seen towering over the well-wooded flat watered by a winding reach of the Thames. Such an outlandish structure bears up the odd name in giving a suggestion of China, not contradicted by the elaborate cultivation around, where all seems market-garden that is not park, buildings, groves or flower-beds. Yet the name, of old written as Kaihough, Kaiho, Kayhoo, and in other quaint forms—for which quay of the howe or hough has been guessed as original—belongs to a thoroughly English parish, whose exotic vegetation, nursed upon a poor soil, came to be twined among many national memories.

25 True Lilies (Common Names)

L	T	E	S	A	T	E	U	G	N	E	B	A	D	R
E	A	S	T	E	R	A	D	T	E	T	O	E	U	A
O	N	V	A	D	A	N	A	C	S	R	Y	S	E	Y
P	O	T	P	O	Q	H	R	Y	A	A	W	O	O	D
A	G	H	S	N	C	E	E	N	R	E	T	S	E	W
R	A	B	U	O	W	L	G	N	I	S	S	G	O	N
D	T	Z	G	M	L	E	E	H	A	N	S	O	N	S
R	R	D	I	E	B	D	N	C	G	D	F	K	O	E
E	A	E	K	L	L	O	E	I	L	R	E	G	I	I
D	M	S	G	O	L	A	L	G	P	L	A	D	P	U
P	L	T	G	I	C	H	Y	D	L	L	Y	Y	D	R
S	Y	B	S	E	T	A	C	O	T	A	A	C	S	I
H	E	N	R	Y	S	A	G	E	R	S	C	A	G	H
W	A	S	H	I	N	G	T	O	N	P	S	Y	E	S
V	A	R	E	S	S	N	A	I	R	E	B	I	S	A

◊ ALPINE LILY
◊ BENGUET LILY
◊ CANADA LILY
◊ CATESBY'S LILY
◊ COAST LILY
◊ EASTER LILY
◊ GOLDEN RAYED LILY
◊ GRAY'S LILY
◊ HANSON'S LILY
◊ HENRY'S LILY
◊ HUMBOLDT'S LILY
◊ KELLEY'S LILY
◊ KELLOGG'S LILY
◊ LEMON LILY
◊ LEOPARD LILY
◊ MARTAGON LILY
◊ ORANGE LILY
◊ ROYAL LILY
◊ SHIRUI LILY
◊ SIBERIAN LILY
◊ TIGER LILY
◊ WASHINGTON LILY
◊ WESTERN LILY
◊ WOOD LILY

26

Deciduous Plants and Trees (Common Names)

◊ AMERICAN SWEETGUM
◊ ARROWWOOD VIBURNUM
◊ BUR OAK
◊ CATALPA
◊ COMMON LILAC
◊ CORNELIAN CHERRY
◊ DIABOLO NINEBARK
◊ EASTERN REDBUD
◊ FLOWERING QUINCE
◊ HARDY HIBISCUS
◊ JAPANESE DOGWOOD
◊ KATSURA
◊ LADY FERN
◊ LOMBARDY POPLAR
◊ NORTHERN CATALPA
◊ OHIO BUCKEYE
◊ PACIFIC POISON OAK
◊ PECAN TREE
◊ QUAKING ASPEN
◊ RIVER BIRCH
◊ SHAGBARK HICKORY
◊ SUGAR MAPLE
◊ VIRGINIA CREEPER
◊ WINTER JASMINE

27 Plants Painted in South America – Marianne North Collection at Kew

A	E	A	R	O	L	H	C	A	R	I	C	A	N	O
X	M	U	I	H	C	N	I	R	Y	S	I	S	A	D
S	E	I	C	H	O	R	N	I	A	M	A	G	T	P
U	S	A	T	S	E	E	A	R	U	T	A	D	E	S
L	T	R	U	M	U	W	D	E	E	N	A	R	H	S
U	T	H	U	N	B	E	R	G	I	A	I	H	P	E
V	J	L	X	U	H	Y	R	C	H	A	S	E	R	A
L	P	A	F	P	T	Z	L	E	N	T	D	D	A	A
O	A	V	E	H	M	U	D	D	C	T	N	Y	T	M
V	Z	N	R	O	S	U	R	I	T	A	A	C	Y	O
E	H	I	U	I	M	A	I	C	A	L	L	H	H	R
I	N	T	A	C	Y	O	O	D	O	E	L	I	C	E
A	P	I	U	O	U	C	P	I	I	A	I	U	A	L
L	A	S	E	O	O	M	V	I	I	S	T	M	T	P
G	P	A	S	S	I	F	L	O	R	A	P	O	S	A

◊ *ATTALEA*
◊ *CARICA PAPAYA*
◊ *CEREUS*
◊ *CHLORAEA*
◊ *CLUSIA*
◊ *COCOS*
◊ *DATURA ARBOREA*
◊ *EICHORNIA AZUREA*
◊ *EPHEDRA ANDINA*
◊ *ERYTHRINA*
◊ *EVOLVULUS*
◊ *HEDYCHIUM*
◊ *IPOMOEA BATATAS*
◊ *MUCUNA*
◊ *PASSIFLORA ALATA*
◊ *PERIANDRA DULCIS*
◊ *PLEROMA*
◊ *PLUMERIA*
◊ *PSIDIUM GUAYAVA*
◊ *SISYRINCHIUM*
◊ *STACHYTARPHETA*
◊ *THUNBERGIA ALATA*
◊ *TILLANDSIA*
◊ *VIOLA MACULATA*

28 Genera in the Family: Myrtaceae – Part One (Myrtle Family)

A	M	Y	R	T	A	S	T	R	U	M	A	R	P	S
M	E	P	B	E	A	U	F	O	R	T	I	A	I	I
A	P	I	L	E	A	N	T	H	U	S	V	E	A	N
E	O	A	L	O	E	M	A	I	Z	N	I	R	I	O
U	C	V	S	E	P	A	O	I	N	E	O	A	B	G
G	T	A	U	C	A	H	Q	M	N	T	O	L	M	A
E	A	U	P	P	H	T	O	E	Y	Y	T	R	Y	S
N	M	G	L	A	J	O	R	S	D	R	E	D	R	A
I	Y	M	O	Z	A	L	L	I	T	R	T	H	O	N
A	R	A	C	C	A	A	R	T	E	E	U	U	C	N
D	T	H	Y	I	T	C	I	M	Z	W	M	M	S	A
R	U	C	L	F	R	E	A	S	S	I	A	O	D	N
A	S	T	A	R	T	E	A	B	S	S	A	S	N	T
A	E	H	C	R	A	M	A	L	G	O	P	A	G	H
A	I	N	I	O	P	L	I	N	I	A	G	E	Y	A

◊ *ACCARA*
◊ *AGONIS*
◊ *AMOMYRTUS*
◊ *ASTARTEA*
◊ *BEAUFORTIA*
◊ *CALOTHAMNUS*
◊ *CALYCOLPUS*
◊ *CHAMGUAVA*
◊ *CHEYNIANA*
◊ *CORYMBIA*
◊ *EREMAEA*
◊ *EUGENIA*
◊ *GOSSIA*
◊ *LAMARCHEA*
◊ *LOPHOSTEMON*
◊ *MYRTASTRUM*
◊ *OCTAMYRTUS*
◊ *PILEANTHUS*
◊ *PLINIA*
◊ *RINZIA*
◊ *SANNANTHA*
◊ *SCHOLTZIA*

29 Genera in the Family: Rosaceae – Part Two (Rose Family)

E	O	D	R	A	A	D	R	A	B	I	L	A	D	B
A	L	O	U	I	S	E	A	N	I	A	L	Z	P	G
X	I	I	F	U	T	N	B	R	D	L	F	O	E	O
S	W	G	B	A	F	S	E	L	I	F	T	W	M	A
N	T	R	U	R	M	H	U	M	G	E	U	M	I	S
L	O	R	L	L	D	O	E	B	R	I	U	R	F	E
S	A	A	A	F	L	H	T	I	O	U	U	W	R	L
I	I	G	M	N	C	A	U	S	W	L	X	N	T	E
B	R	R	P	L	V	M	F	X	O	A	O	A	A	M
B	E	I	A	D	L	A	L	C	S	N	I	I	F	O
A	C	M	Y	A	C	A	E	N	A	S	E	B	R	R
L	N	O	S	U	L	I	P	S	E	M	W	D	O	E
D	E	N	G	J	V	D	O	V	I	R	S	S	A	T
I	P	I	H	F	U	S	I	J	B	A	A	L	O	E
A	S	A	M	E	L	A	N	C	H	I	E	R	I	H

◊ *ACAENA*
◊ *ADENOSTOMA*
◊ *AGRIMONIA*
◊ *ALCHEMILLA*
◊ *AMELANCHIER*
◊ *COLURIA*
◊ *DALIBARDA*
◊ *ERIOLOBUS*
◊ *FALLUGIA*
◊ *GEUM*
◊ *HETEROMELES*
◊ *IVESIA*
◊ *LOUISEANIA*
◊ *MESPILUS*
◊ *POTERIUM*
◊ *ROSA*
◊ *SIBBALDIA*
◊ *SORBUS*
◊ *SPENCERIA*
◊ *STRANVAESIA*

30

Plants in *The Complete Herbal* by Nicholas Culpeper – Part One

◊ BARBERRY
◊ BEECH TREE
◊ BORRAGE
◊ CENTAURY
◊ CHERVIL
◊ CLARY
◊ CUDWEED
◊ DARNEL
◊ GARLICK
◊ HENBANE
◊ HOPS
◊ LAVENDER
◊ LETTUCE
◊ LIQUORICE
◊ MADDER
◊ MALLOW
◊ MUSTARD
◊ PARSNIP
◊ SCABIOUS
◊ SPIGNEL
◊ VERVAIN
◊ WATER BETONY
◊ WHEAT
◊ YARROW

31 The History of Botany

- ◊ ABU AL-ABBAS AL-NABATI
- ◊ ANCIENT GREECE
- ◊ AVESTAN WRITINGS
- ◊ *BOOK OF PLANTS*
- ◊ CONRAD VON GESNER
- ◊ *DISPENSATORIUM*
- ◊ *ENQUIRY INTO PLANTS*
- ◊ HERBALISM
- ◊ HIERONYMUS BOCK
- ◊ *HISTORIA PLANTARUM*
- ◊ *HUANGDI NEIJING*, CHINA
- ◊ IBN BASSAL
- ◊ JOHN GERARD
- ◊ LEONHART FUCHS
- ◊ *MANUSMRUTI*, INDIA
- ◊ *NABATEAN AGRICULTURE*
- ◊ OTTO BRUNFELS
- ◊ PADUA BOTANICAL GARDEN, ITALY
- ◊ ROBERT HOOKE
- ◊ THEOPHRASTUS
- ◊ ULISSE ALDROVANDI
- ◊ UNIVERSITY OF OXFORD BOTANIC GARDEN
- ◊ VALERIUS CORDUS

32 Unusual Plant Nicknames – Part One

D E E W E Z E E N S N C N I D
S E H C T I W A L M H O V E X
U T T S G F I I A E O W L R Z
R F A D U I V D E L E B A G M
Y U J R E E D S L D M E T O S
G T I A D O E A E A S T N O S
N Y R P G W B E R B G K E S T
I D Q O E C L C M T E N I E A
C N L E W B S A D Y G J D F O
N A D L E E L L I O N S E O G
A C O S W A L C R E T S B O L
D S O S I R E P T E A T O T I
S N N M Z E S A P H E W O R M
Y E P I N C U S H I O N S A A
H E G A S U A S K U N K A R D

◊ BALLOON FLOWER
◊ CANDYTUFT
◊ CHEESEWEED
◊ DANCING GIRL GINGER
◊ DEVIL'S WALKINGSTICK
◊ GOAT'S BEARD
◊ GOOSEFOOT
◊ HENS AND CHICKS
◊ LAMB'S-EAR
◊ LEOPARD'S BANE
◊ LION'S EAR
◊ LOBSTER-CLAWS
◊ MAD DOG SKULLCAP
◊ MONKEY NO-CLIMB
◊ NIPPLEWORT
◊ NOSEBLEED
◊ OBEDIENT PLANT
◊ PINCUSHIONS
◊ SAUSAGE TREE
◊ SCRAMBLED EGGS
◊ SKUNK CABBAGE
◊ SNEEZEWEED
◊ TOAD LILY
◊ WITCHES' BUTTER

33

Botanical Artists and Illustrators – Part Two

N	O	S	N	I	K	R	A	P	R	J	E	R	A	S
S	T	W	I	N	I	N	G	B	P	E	L	L	O	E
L	O	E	H	M	R	O	W	A	N	E	S	B	O	Y
E	C	W	I	S	E	N	O	T	S	F	O	S	D	I
M	L	O	E	R	C	H	A	Y	H	Z	E	N	O	N
O	I	B	N	R	B	Y	R	U	I	D	O	N	E	R
Y	H	E	G	A	B	U	W	C	O	C	Y	A	N	D
N	S	S	C	S	B	Y	A	H	I	C	O	F	M	Y
E	U	B	E	A	B	E	R	H	A	E	C	K	E	L
L	K	T	J	J	S	B	R	L	M	E	N	M	R	E
O	A	S	E	E	J	P	N	E	C	N	L	I	I	N
C	T	I	O	B	P	M	A	R	K	A	G	N	A	C
Q	U	I	H	V	I	P	Y	R	E	O	I	N	N	A
U	F	A	S	L	E	M	E	G	I	R	K	A	I	G
R	E	T	G	P	N	S	E	V	R	U	P	S	O	K

- ◊ CLAUDE AUBRIET
- ◊ TIFFANY BOZIC
- ◊ PRISCILLA SUSAN BURY
- ◊ CLAUS CASPARI
- ◊ MARK CATESBY
- ◊ ELIZABETH CONABERE
- ◊ GILLIAN CONDY
- ◊ YOSHIO FUTAKUSHI
- ◊ JANICE GLIMN-LACY
- ◊ ERNST HAECKEL
- ◊ BARBARA JEPPE
- ◊ SALLY KEIR
- ◊ MARTHA KING
- ◊ JACQUES LE MOYNE
- ◊ MARIA SIBYLLA MERIAN
- ◊ SYDNEY PARKINSON
- ◊ EMILY PELLOE
- ◊ RODELLA PURVES
- ◊ SARAH RHODES
- ◊ CELIA ROSSER
- ◊ ELLIS ROWAN
- ◊ JAMES SOWERBY
- ◊ MARGARET STONES
- ◊ ELIZABETH TWINING

34

Genera in the Family: Asteraceae – Part Two (Daisy Family)

```
A A A A I H E T E R O M E R A
I E I A I L A T P A H C S A I
B L R N C S Q L K C A L I E R
B L E C A R E O U P M J T A O
E I N E S Z E R A N C O C T D
B A R M H H U P A C I A A N A
E C E P N Q U L A O B I G A R
R S W E L A A E A E S S I M T
A E O X C P S Z O Z Y R L I E
S L E A S U H T N A B E O H P
A T L A L I S E A R A V S C E
A I N I D A T T I V H A D U A
A A A T E P H R O S E R I S W
B W A M R E P S O R E T E H E
A I H C T I F S I L E C A F G
```

- ◊ *BEBBIA*
- ◊ *CAESULIA*
- ◊ *CHAPTALIA*
- ◊ *CHIMANTAEA*
- ◊ *FACELIS*
- ◊ *FITCHIA*
- ◊ *HETEROMERA*
- ◊ *HETEROSPERMA*
- ◊ *INULA*
- ◊ *KOEHNEOLA*
- ◊ *LAPSANA*
- ◊ *LESCAILLEA*
- ◊ *OLIGACTIS*
- ◊ *PAPUACALIA*
- ◊ *PETRADORIA*
- ◊ *PHOEBANTHUS*
- ◊ *SOARESIA*
- ◊ *TEPHROSERIS*
- ◊ *TRAVERSIA*
- ◊ *VITTADINIA*
- ◊ *WERNERIA*
- ◊ *ZALUZANIA*

35 Extinct Prehistoric Plant Species and Genera – Part One

M U L L Y H P O N E H P S P S
S S P H E N O B A I E R A G C
I H C Y F S E S A P C Z I G H
G Y A A M I Y R A N X N L A M
I I E U N Y Y L O L K O I K E
L S N L A N E R M G S S T E I
L D E W I O U M O S S C I N S
A A W T P M R L O L A A H A S
R I W A I O S P A L L I Y I N
I R N L O M T T A R L A L C E
A A C S B E A M V L I F M U R
X G E X R V I Z S C Q A Y M I
N A T I Q T N I L S S O N I A
E S S P E I V A N O F E N S E
D R O S E R A P O L L I S G L

◊ *ACER HILLSI*

◊ *ACER IVANOFENSE*

◊ *ACER KENAICUM*

◊ *ACER SMILEYI*

◊ *ANNULARIA STELLATA*

◊ *BANKSIA KINGII*

◊ *CALAMITES*

◊ *DROSERAPOLLIS*

◊ *GINKGO CRANEI*

◊ *GLOSSOPTERIS*

◊ *NILSSONIA*

◊ *OSMUNDA WEHRII*

◊ *PALEOPANAX*

◊ *RHUS MALLORYI*

◊ *RHUS ROOSEAE*

◊ *SAGARIA*

◊ *SCHMEISSNERIA*

◊ *SIGILLARIA*

◊ *SPHENOBAIERA*

◊ *SPHENOPHYLLUM*

◊ *TILIA JOHNSONI*

◊ *ZAMITES*

Old-Growth Forest Areas

P	A	L	R	G	E	A	K	A	O	E	U	L	B	E
S	L	A	K	A	K	A	M	E	G	A	B	E	L	T
H	A	R	W	S	E	W	A	R	D	R	H	O	C	A
W	B	D	H	E	B	B	U	O	E	L	F	F	L	S
E	S	E	D	A	S	M	E	Z	H	E	C	S	A	T
P	T	H	X	L	A	T	T	T	R	T	A	I	Y	R
J	T	T	T	S	E	L	E	N	I	K	X	P	O	I
E	E	A	R	O	E	R	B	R	S	H	X	S	Q	L
R	L	C	E	M	L	A	S	D	N	E	W	E	U	L
R	L	L	U	D	N	N	A	K	R	I	H	Y	O	E
A	O	A	A	K	Y	R	N	A	M	L	L	I	T	M
N	P	U	F	V	G	S	N	E	L	G	E	C	I	A
E	R	D	I	O	C	R	A	W	F	O	R	D	H	R
S	A	R	I	P	R	T	A	R	K	I	N	E	F	K
Y	I	B	J	A	D	T	B	E	T	D	E	D	E	A

- ◊ BAXTER STATE PARK
- ◊ BELT WOODS
- ◊ BIOGRADSKA GORA
- ◊ BLUE OAK WOODLANDS
- ◊ CATHEDRAL PINES
- ◊ CLAYOQUOT SOUND
- ◊ CRAWFORD NOTCH
- ◊ DYSART WOODS
- ◊ FERNBANK FOREST
- ◊ FORT LEAVENWORTH
- ◊ HIRKAN NATIONAL PARK
- ◊ ICE GLEN
- ◊ KAKAMEGA FOREST
- ◊ MELTZER WOODS
- ◊ POLLETT'S COVE
- ◊ SADDLER'S WOODS
- ◊ SEWARD PARK
- ◊ SIPSEY WILDERNESS
- ◊ TARKINE
- ◊ TILLMAN RAVINE
- ◊ TRILLEMARKA
- ◊ VALLE CERVARA
- ◊ WESTERN CAUCASUS
- ◊ WHITE BEAR FOREST

37 Trees of Oceania (Common Names)

S A P E R S A N R A H G M A J
V A R Y W I G P A P T U M I R
S F X H R A D H D I G A S H D
A A I I I H S I E N T U W I E
R T R O P U T R C K T V D A I
E U F J R A I T A P R N E Q U
P U I B K A A R Y U N L L U L
T A M K R H A L F E P E M A B
W I U A I K A A V R H G E S A
H P T T A C Y T U N O C O C D
R C I O U S H P P I E N G F N
U A A E K Q O P O R R S U N U
N W Z E R I V E R O A U L B G
I K R A B R E P A P R M A A Y
E U J D O O W H G U O D U K F

- ◊ BEACH CORDIA
- ◊ BRUSH BLOODWOOD
- ◊ CEDAR WATTLE
- ◊ COCONUT
- ◊ DOUGHWOOD
- ◊ DROOPY LEAF
- ◊ EUCALYPTUS
- ◊ FALSE ARALIA
- ◊ GUNDABLUIE
- ◊ KARAKA
- ◊ KAURI
- ◊ NGAIO
- ◊ NIPA PALM
- ◊ PAPERBARK
- ◊ PUKKATI
- ◊ PURIRI
- ◊ PURPLE CORALTREE
- ◊ RIMU
- ◊ RIVER JAM
- ◊ TAHITIAN CHESTNUT
- ◊ TARAIRE
- ◊ TAWA
- ◊ TITOKI
- ◊ WHITE MANGROVE

38 Evergreens (Common Names)

M S E L E V S R A P A P E I Y
A A N R E T N I W F I H R A E
D P E D O R R Y A E L A Z A R
R B L C E M U W I W L E F J E
O U S T A C A M S C E W A O T
N A S L E R O H E C M P C C N
E E E N I U X M O E A I R S O
W F F Z N R L A M N C U E A M
S L O T A L S B E O I V P L N
Z N A R E T A S S T N A I G E
A I A D T L E M L E Z K N U F
N E H J S U X C V H C B U O A
B I G A U I N I S A O E J D S
U Y M S U H L E J X W H I T E
D A Y E N O T R S G O R C E A

◊ ARIZONA CYPRESS
◊ AZALEA
◊ BALSAM FIR
◊ BLUE SPRUCE
◊ BOX
◊ CAMELLIA
◊ COAST REDWOOD
◊ COMMON YEW
◊ DOUGLAS FIR
◊ FORTUNE'S SPINDLE
◊ GIANT SEQUOIA
◊ JACK PINE
◊ JAPANESE LAUREL
◊ JUNIPER
◊ LIVE OAK
◊ MADRONE
◊ MAHONIA
◊ MONTEREY PINE
◊ MOUNTAIN HEMLOCK
◊ SCOTS PINE
◊ THUJA
◊ WESTERN RED CEDAR
◊ WHITE FIR
◊ WINTER DAPHNE

39 Sunflowers (Common Names)

X O D A R A P M I C E G U X M
T T H I N L E A F H A I R Y L
F F I T S N A M T R E S E D A
I E X R W H A D X J N S D I N
H O H P A R L I I R I N N E O
E T P N M A K B L R B R E W Z
C H O C P Y A L E I O J L O I
U P R O H L L M A F M L S O R
S R T H M E I N I K M I F D A
I A E B I S E L O G E L X L U
C I R F I S A R X M I S T A A
K R S W W C Y L F S M A I N M
S I D M W B P C R U L O N D W
L E H T O O T W A S L B C T E
F N R E T S E W H G A Z D G W

◊ ALKALI
◊ ARIZONA
◊ CALIFORNIA
◊ CHEERFUL
◊ COMMON
◊ CUSICK'S
◊ DESERT
◊ FLORIDA
◊ GIANT
◊ HAIRY
◊ LAKESIDE
◊ MAXIMILIAN
◊ PARADOX
◊ PORTER'S
◊ PRAIRIE
◊ RAYLESS
◊ SAWTOOTH
◊ SLENDER
◊ SMOOTH
◊ STIFF
◊ SWAMP
◊ THINLEAF
◊ WESTERN
◊ WOODLAND

40 Botanical Terms – Part Two

E	S	N	O	I	S	S	I	C	S	B	A	L	E	D
T	T	A	Y	M	O	O	L	B	T	B	E	S	R	J
A	R	U	D	E	R	A	L	H	A	M	R	O	N	E
N	O	R	A	L	E	A	Y	S	M	L	B	O	M	G
D	J	U	G	U	M	M	S	A	E	W	P	O	F	Y
A	L	H	R	A	C	E	M	E	N	F	Z	U	Y	N
H	A	Z	S	D	P	L	C	L	Q	I	Z	F	A	O
L	T	L	N	A	O	Y	I	C	H	S	Y	B	G	P
R	E	E	L	A	N	X	I	R	A	U	G	L	L	H
O	P	G	Z	R	S	M	B	E	B	Q	O	A	O	O
H	P	U	B	E	S	C	E	N	T	C	T	O	B	R
W	O	M	T	O	O	T	H	E	D	O	E	M	O	E
A	E	E	L	L	A	M	Y	N	C	N	A	V	S	Y
A	L	F	T	E	T	B	Y	I	N	V	Y	N	E	V
S	S	I	E	M	N	O	D	E	L	Y	T	O	C	Z

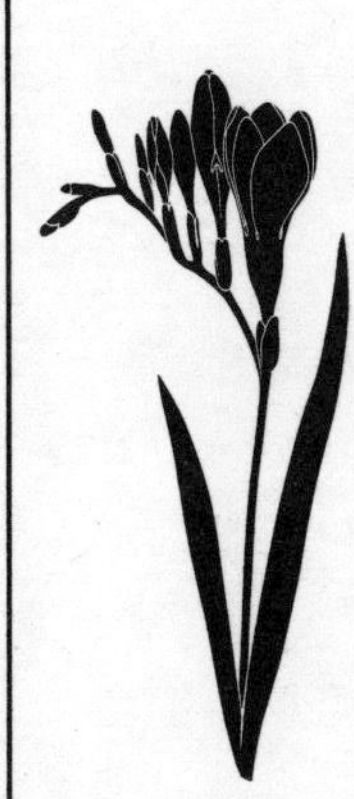

◊ ABSCISSION
◊ ADNATE
◊ AREOLE
◊ BLOOM
◊ COTYLEDON
◊ DICOT
◊ FORB
◊ GLOBOSE
◊ GYNOPHORE
◊ JUGUM
◊ LEGUME
◊ LEMMA
◊ MALLEE
◊ PETAL
◊ PUBESCENT
◊ RACEME
◊ RHIZOME
◊ RUDERAL
◊ SEPAL
◊ STAMEN
◊ TOOTHED
◊ WHORL
◊ XYLEM
◊ ZYGOTE

41 Ancient Trees (Age)

P	H	V	I	N	E	Y	E	E	A	S	K	N	T	I
H	A	L	E	S	U	H	T	E	M	U	M	L	G	T
A	E	N	W	N	N	G	P	C	S	C	A	E	N	E
J	E	A	K	L	I	W	L	R	E	I	N	A	N	Y
A	L	F	R	E	S	D	O	N	I	E	R	A	R	G
O	S	T	E	T	U	P	R	A	R	T	R	P	Z	R
Z	Y	C	A	B	A	Y	S	A	A	H	A	M	K	A
B	D	R	O	C	E	A	L	K	J	L	I	O	E	N
D	A	C	O	F	R	N	A	X	M	U	N	T	K	I
I	E	K	A	V	I	C	N	T	L	G	T	H	N	T
U	R	W	E	I	O	E	T	E	E	X	R	E	E	O
A	B	J	N	K	B	A	L	E	T	R	E	R	P	A
B	V	A	N	L	O	F	G	D	B	T	E	L	R	K
E	V	U	V	T	H	E	V	W	I	N	T	R	A	S
R	A	L	L	E	N	N	O	C	Y	L	L	A	B	L

◊ BALLYCONNELL YEW, IRELAND (EST. 2000-5000)

◊ BENNETT JUNIPER, USA (EST. 3000)

◊ GENERAL SHERMAN, USA (EST. 2300-2700)

◊ GRANIT OAK, BULGARIA (EST. 1600)

◊ JARDINE JUNIPER, USA (EST. 1500)

◊ KOCA KATRAN, TURKEY (EST. 2022)

◊ KOCA PORSUK, TURKEY (EST. 4112)

◊ KONGEEGEN, DENMARK (EST. 1500-2000)

◊ METHUSELAH, USA (4850+)

◊ MOTHER OF THE FOREST, USA (†2520)

◊ PANKE BAOBAB, ZIMBABWE (†2450)

◊ RAINTREE, USA (EST. 3000)

◊ SARV-E ABARKUH, IRAN (EST. 4000+)

◊ SCOFIELD JUNIPER, USA (EST. †2675)

◊ STARA MASLINA, MONTENEGRO (EST. 2000)

◊ TNJRI, AZERBAIJAN (EST. 2000+)

42 Percy Bysshe Shelley – *The Flower That Smiles To-day* (1821–22)

The flower that smiles to-day
To-morrow dies;
All that we wish to stay
Tempts and then flies.
What is this world's delight?
Lightning that mocks the night,
Brief even as bright.

Virtue, how frail it is!
Friendship how rare!
Love, how it sells poor bliss
For proud despair!
But we, though soon they fall,
Survive their joy, and all
Which ours we call.

Whilst skies are blue and bright,
Whilst flowers are gay,
Whilst eyes that change ere night
Make glad the day;
Whilst yet the calm hours creep,
Dream thou—and from thy sleep
Then wake to weep.

43 Rare Plants

O	S	U	B	R	O	S	E	R	Y	S	I	M	U	M
Y	C	D	E	C	E	N	Y	G	O	N	E	T	S	F
C	S	E	N	C	E	P	H	A	L	A	R	T	O	S
O	H	D	Y	A	T	A	R	N	I	M	R	H	A	T
A	O	U	G	I	I	E	S	E	R	M	M	R	C	A
T	R	B	A	L	A	T	A	A	A	A	A	Y	A	H
O	E	A	S	E	Y	T	N	C	V	R	D	Z	C	I
A	A	U	U	K	T	A	M	A	E	G	E	N	I	N
I	I	T	D	C	H	A	R	R	N	O	L	I	A	A
L	S	I	E	A	A	J	X	D	E	N	R	U	C	A
O	A	A	M	H	I	R	L	U	A	A	E	Z	C	I
N	D	I	L	G	A	L	I	G	S	I	S	P	Y	D
G	S	A	C	E	R	D	E	A	S	E	P	G	C	U
A	I	M	E	L	L	O	W	X	R	A	D	E	A	R
M	V	I	P	M	U	I	C	A	R	E	I	H	S	C

◊ *ACACIA ANEGADENSIS*

◊ *ANOGRAMMA ASCENSIONIS*

◊ *ARAUCARIA ANGUSTIFOLIA*

◊ *CRUDIA BIBUNDINA*

◊ *CYCAS TANSACHANA*

◊ *DRACAENA CINNABARI*

◊ *DUBAUTIA LATIFOLIA*

◊ *DYPSIS AMBOSITRAE*

◊ *ENCEPHALARTOS WOODII*

◊ *ERYSIMUM MENZIESII*

◊ *HACKELIA VENUSTA*

◊ *HIERACIUM SNOWDONIENSE*

◊ *ILEX MACHILIFOLIA*

◊ *MAGNOLIA JARDINENSIS*

◊ *MEDUSAGYNE OPPOSITIFOLIA*

◊ *PENNANTIA BAYLISIANA*

◊ *RAVENEA MUSICALIS*

◊ *SHOREA SEMINIS*

◊ *SORBUS LEYANA*

◊ *STENOGYNE KANEHOANA*

◊ *TAHINA SPECTABILIS*

◊ *TAXUS FLORIDANA*

◊ *WOLLEMIA NOBILIS*

◊ *ZAMIA PRASINA*

44 Plant-Related Last Names

A	S	O	N	I	P	S	E	S	A	N	D	I	L	E
T	O	H	O	L	L	I	N	S	E	S	T	F	E	O
A	N	S	W	N	Z	G	P	A	R	L	P	H	R	L
F	Q	U	K	E	R	N	E	R	A	E	A	E	I	A
A	N	B	L	D	C	I	F	M	L	W	D	S	N	F
Y	P	L	A	N	T	E	L	U	T	L	O	S	O	O
M	Y	A	G	I	N	A	T	H	J	G	A	U	L	R
S	A	B	E	L	P	N	O	U	J	I	B	A	J	A
D	M	N	R	E	R	R	N	M	N	R	M	E	G	G
U	W	P	D	L	N	G	O	A	V	E	J	O	J	V
L	O	R	T	E	G	A	W	K	M	T	R	U	T	W
A	L	A	S	R	L	O	O	O	U	T	U	J	H	O
B	S	D	E	E	R	D	F	H	A	I	W	E	M	H
H	C	N	E	D	B	E	S	L	B	G	I	D	U	P
M	A	T	S	U	O	K	A	P	P	L	E	T	O	N

◊ APPLETON
◊ ASH
◊ ASPEN
◊ BAUM
◊ BUSH
◊ DE PALMA
◊ ESPINOSA
◊ FUJIMOTO
◊ GAROFALO
◊ HAWTHORNE
◊ HOLLINS
◊ KERNER

◊ KOHL
◊ LAGER
◊ LINDEN
◊ LJUNGGREN
◊ MANDEL
◊ MATSUOKA
◊ ORTEGA
◊ PLANT
◊ REED
◊ RETTIG
◊ ROSALES
◊ ROWAN

45 Book and Story Title Plants

C	S	U	C	O	R	C	A	L	Y	B	T	E	P	P
L	I	N	O	G	E	L	I	U	R	Y	U	E	D	A
A	I	T	F	I	G	L	L	O	R	A	L	O	T	M
R	T	G	T	E	Y	Z	O	T	A	C	I	N	S	A
G	F	I	R	A	Z	K	T	E	R	W	P	U	R	R
E	A	N	V	E	L	S	U	U	I	Y	T	N	O	I
T	O	G	A	Y	E	S	S	L	Y	P	S	O	L	G
N	Y	Y	N	F	S	N	L	A	Y	U	X	I	E	O
I	H	V	W	E	D	O	W	L	R	T	U	L	A	L
D	B	N	R	N	W	A	A	O	E	W	I	E	N	D
I	R	P	R	S	R	C	H	A	O	L	N	D	D	E
H	Y	E	G	A	U	F	R	L	A	D	A	N	E	C
C	F	O	F	E	I	O	O	C	I	R	O	A	R	A
R	S	N	E	T	S	E	S	U	Q	A	A	D	P	S
O	P	Y	H	E	U	N	S	D	E	S	E	R	T	T

- ◊ *A TREE GROWS IN BROOKLYN*
- ◊ *DAISY MILLER*
- ◊ *DANDELION WINE*
- ◊ *EMPRESS ORCHID*
- ◊ *EUCALYPTUS*
- ◊ *FLOWERS FOR ALGERNON*
- ◊ *FLOWERS IN THE ATTIC*
- ◊ *LILY AND THE OCTOPUS*
- ◊ *MAGIC FOR MARIGOLD*
- ◊ *PEONY*
- ◊ *SAD CYPRESS*
- ◊ *THE BLACK DAHLIA*
- ◊ *THE BLACK TULIP*
- ◊ *THE DESERT ROSE*
- ◊ *THE INTEGRAL TREES*
- ◊ *THE LOTUS EATERS*
- ◊ *THE MAGIC FARAWAY TREE*
- ◊ *THE TEA ROSE*
- ◊ *THE WIND IN THE WILLOWS*
- ◊ *UNDER THE GREENWOOD TREE*
- ◊ *UNDER THE LILACS*
- ◊ *WHERE THE RED FERN GROWS*
- ◊ *WHITE OLEANDER*
- ◊ *YELLOW CROCUS*

46

People with Flowers or Plants Named after them

◊ INGRID BERGMAN
◊ WILLIAM BLIGH
◊ JULIA CHILD
◊ MARIE CURIE
◊ JUDI DENCH
◊ ALBERT EINSTEIN
◊ BENJAMIN FRANKLIN
◊ LADY GAGA
◊ JIMI HENDRIX
◊ AUDREY HEPBURN
◊ JULIO IGLESIAS
◊ THOMAS JEFFERSON
◊ GRACE KELLY
◊ FREDDIE MERCURY
◊ HELEN MIRREN
◊ CLAUDE MONET
◊ MARILYN MONROE
◊ MICHELLE OBAMA
◊ DOLLY PARTON
◊ FRANKLIN D. ROOSEVELT
◊ ELIZABETH TAYLOR
◊ TINA TURNER
◊ QUEEN VICTORIA
◊ BETTY WHITE

47 Genera in the Family: Orchidaceae – Part Two (Orchid Family)

A	C	I	A	N	T	H	U	S	I	D	E	N	I	A
V	A	S	I	S	P	O	N	E	A	L	A	H	P	A
A	V	M	T	V	A	R	A	D	I	L	M	O	D	E
R	A	A	E	M	L	N	I	L	L	U	I	S	I	A
M	P	L	L	B	U	C	D	E	O	L	J	P	L	L
O	O	A	B	L	H	I	I	E	A	J	A	I	E	L
D	S	R	L	A	E	N	C	L	R	C	J	M	E	Y
O	T	P	E	O	I	Y	L	Y	H	E	U	A	H	H
R	A	A	Y	U	E	E	O	I	R	R	L	I	T	P
U	S	U	Q	L	E	L	T	L	E	O	R	L	N	I
M	I	C	X	R	A	E	A	L	E	G	C	L	A	S
L	A	R	R	O	S	C	L	G	E	D	E	E	U	A
J	E	A	S	D	P	A	I	Z	L	O	T	S	E	B
S	W	I	S	T	A	U	I	E	O	G	E	N	L	E
C	O	E	L	I	O	P	S	I	S	H	W	A	E	H

- ◊ *ACIANTHUS*
- ◊ *ANSELLIA*
- ◊ *APOSTASIA*
- ◊ *ARMODORUM*
- ◊ *AUXOPUS*
- ◊ *BASIPHYLLAEA*
- ◊ *BLETIA*
- ◊ *CALYPSO*
- ◊ *COELIOPSIS*
- ◊ *CORYCIUM*
- ◊ *DICHAEA*
- ◊ *ELOYELLA*
- ◊ *EUANTHE*
- ◊ *GALEOLA*
- ◊ *JACQUINIELLA*
- ◊ *LEMURELLA*
- ◊ *LUISIA*
- ◊ *PACHITES*
- ◊ *PHALAENOPSIS*
- ◊ *SANDERELLA*
- ◊ *STOLZIA*
- ◊ *WARREELLA*

48 IUCN Red List – Extinct in the Wild

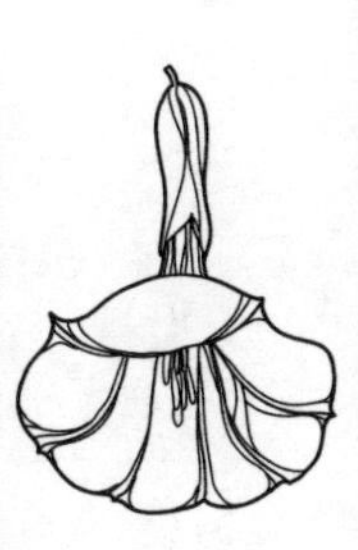

- ◊ *ABUTILON PITCAIRNENSE*
- ◊ *BRUGMANSIA ARBOREA*
- ◊ *BRUGMANSIA AUREA*
- ◊ *BRUGMANSIA INSIGNIS*
- ◊ *BRUGMANSIA SUAVEOLENS*
- ◊ *BRUGMANSIA VERSICOLOR*
- ◊ *CAMELLIA AMPLEXICAULIS*
- ◊ *CORYPHA TALIERA*
- ◊ *CYANEA PINNATIFIDA*
- ◊ *CYANEA SUPERBA*
- ◊ *CYANEA TRUNCATA*
- ◊ *ENCEPHALARTOS RELICTUS*
- ◊ *ENCEPHALARTOS WOODII*
- ◊ *EUPHORBIA MAYURNATHANII*
- ◊ *FRANKLINIA ALATAMAHA*
- ◊ *KOKIA COOKEI*
- ◊ *MANGIFERA CASTURI*
- ◊ *MANGIFERA RUBROPETALA*
- ◊ *NYMPHAEA THERMARUM*
- ◊ *SENECIO LEUCOPEPLUS*
- ◊ *SOPHORA TOROMIRO*
- ◊ *TERMINALIA ACUMINATA*

49 Genera in the Family: Brassicaceae – Part One (Cabbage Family)

A	I	N	W	T	H	E	L	Y	P	O	D	I	U	M
A	O	N	V	E	S	U	N	A	S	Y	H	T	A	A
H	M	W	P	E	R	A	Y	C	N	I	O	C	E	R
M	B	U	F	S	F	D	A	D	A	V	E	N	L	E
A	U	E	I	F	U	M	E	S	A	O	P	M	G	H
A	E	I	R	D	B	H	A	R	I	Y	G	I	N	T
L	I	N	D	O	I	R	T	H	M	R	A	A	I	N
I	J	N	P	O	E	P	F	N	C	A	E	D	R	A
H	V	U	I	I	H	I	E	A	A	R	N	B	P	L
P	S	F	R	R	D	T	U	L	R	C	O	N	I	E
O	H	O	I	A	U	D	H	O	T	S	L	U	I	T
I	M	W	H	C	L	A	S	C	D	X	E	A	G	A
L	S	O	R	Y	U	L	R	F	O	S	N	T	H	M
E	A	A	I	H	C	I	E	R	D	L	E	H	I	C
H	A	I	K	C	E	R	E	V	I	H	C	S	F	A

◊ *ATELANTHERA*

◊ *ATHYSANUS*

◊ *AURINIA*

◊ *CHALCANTHUS*

◊ *COINCYA*

◊ *FARSETIA*

◊ *HELDREICHIA*

◊ *HELIOPHILA*

◊ *IBERIS*

◊ *IDAHOA*

◊ *LEPIDIUM*

◊ *MORIERA*

◊ *NEVADA*

◊ *OCHTHODIUM*

◊ *PRINGLEA*

◊ *SCAMBOPUS*

◊ *SCHIVERECKIA*

◊ *THELYPODIUM*

◊ *VELLA*

◊ *WERDERMANNIA*

50 Flowering Plant Families (Common Names)

```
D F S D E E W D N I B I T E A
A I U I I Y W I C E P L A N T
I A H J Y O E L L C R I N P E
F G T C D A I L E M O R B E E
I U N C R J Y B S G T T A M A
G M A A N O P U C R E T T U B
W A C B R W H L R W A G F Y B
O D A B D D T E H E V P M R E
R D H A X O A R G C P A B L N
T E A G P G E U F R L P T B B
U R L E B B H A D L U R E U O
G E N T I A N L O A Y P A P R
A V U C T N X W E M I A S E A
C T E A D E C A C T U S H O G
T T L P H T N A R A M A Y F E
```

◊ ACANTHUS
◊ AMARANTH
◊ BINDWEED
◊ BORAGE
◊ BROMELIAD
◊ BUTTERCUP
◊ CABBAGE
◊ CACTUS
◊ DAISY
◊ DOGBANE
◊ FIGWORT
◊ GENTIAN
◊ HEATH
◊ ICE PLANT
◊ LAUREL
◊ MADDER
◊ MALLOW
◊ MYRTLE
◊ NETTLE
◊ ORCHID
◊ PARSLEY
◊ PEPPER
◊ PROTEA
◊ SPURGE

51 IUCN Red List Critically Endangered – Part Two (Common Names)

S	M	L	N	E	M	O	D	G	E	D	Y	S	A	D
Y	O	A	G	H	I	A	V	W	H	E	C	D	S	O
E	D	A	N	I	H	A	T	H	A	V	I	C	C	U
S	A	O	T	N	H	H	C	N	E	R	F	A	E	G
A	A	R	A	L	S	D	S	U	R	V	F	R	N	U
C	E	H	S	T	O	G	N	A	U	E	S	O	S	M
E	L	T	T	O	B	A	T	L	G	T	S	L	I	W
S	U	V	W	F	I	S	E	A	O	G	T	I	O	O
H	G	X	H	S	E	T	B	B	J	N	T	N	N	O
I	O	W	R	U	T	B	C	D	V	C	E	E	B	D
B	G	A	L	E	A	E	N	E	S	E	L	S	T	S
S	K	B	I	C	I	T	H	R	I	W	T	A	A	D
N	O	R	E	W	A	X	E	N	N	A	R	L	Y	V
O	A	H	G	A	P	S	A	M	A	K	A	N	X	S
P	R	I	B	B	Y	C	G	M	I	D	B	Y	E	M

◊ AKAMAS CENTAURY
◊ ASCENSION SPURGE
◊ BARTLETT'S RATA
◊ BLUE STAR
◊ BOTTLE PALM
◊ BOXWOOD
◊ CAROLINE'S PINK
◊ CASEY'S LARKSPUR
◊ CLAY'S HIBISCUS
◊ DWARF ILIAU
◊ FRENCH GRASS
◊ GUMWOOD
◊ HE CABBAGE TREE
◊ KARSIAN NONEA
◊ MANN'S GARDENIA
◊ NGOTSHE CYCAD
◊ PARIETTE CACTUS
◊ PRIBBY
◊ RED BALAU
◊ SALAD PLANT
◊ SINAI PRIMROSE
◊ TAHINA PALM
◊ VAHL'S BOXWOOD
◊ WAXEN CYCAD

52

Poems with Titles Relating to Plants and Trees

Y	M	I	L	O	U	E	N	S	E	H	C	R	I	B
J	S	H	T	L	I	U	O	B	I	U	S	E	E	R
E	C	I	V	U	E	F	S	Y	L	O	L	E	A	F
E	S	H	A	D	L	D	I	U	P	O	A	T	R	F
R	D	F	E	D	N	I	O	D	M	I	S	K	E	X
T	A	L	N	R	S	E	P	H	X	M	T	S	W	R
E	F	O	A	T	R	R	T	S	P	S	E	A	O	C
M	F	W	P	P	G	Y	F	T	E	S	G	R	L	M
I	O	E	R	E	P	P	R	I	L	A	A	T	F	F
L	D	R	B	C	O	L	L	I	R	E	V	T	N	G
D	I	S	O	P	R	E	E	D	P	X	S	O	U	G
X	L	L	L	S	V	M	E	T	T	E	U	D	S	E
C	S	A	Y	O	E	N	J	B	R	P	G	A	S	L
D	R	E	L	W	T	R	A	E	H	E	E	Y	C	I
S	U	L	A	C	E	E	R	T	R	A	E	P	R	N

- ◊ *A POISON TREE*
- ◊ *AH! SUN-FLOWER*
- ◊ *ASPHODEL, THAT GREENY FLOWER*
- ◊ *BIRCHES*
- ◊ *BINSEY POPLARS*
- ◊ *CHERRY-RIPE*
- ◊ *ELIOT'S OAK*
- ◊ *LOVELIEST OF TREES*
- ◊ *PEAR TREE*
- ◊ *TALL NETTLES*
- ◊ *THE BLOSSOM*
- ◊ *THE DAISY FOLLOWS SOFT THE SUN*
- ◊ *THE DEATH OF THE FLOWERS*
- ◊ *THE FALL OF THE LEAF*
- ◊ *THE FLOWER THAT SMILES TO-DAY*
- ◊ *THE GARDEN OF LOVE*
- ◊ *THE HEART OF THE TREE*
- ◊ *THE LAST ROSE OF SUMMER*
- ◊ *THE LILY*
- ◊ *THE OLD APPLE-TREE*
- ◊ *THE SICK ROSE*
- ◊ *THIS LIME-TREE BOWER MY PRISON*
- ◊ *TO DAFFODILS*
- ◊ *TULIPS*

53

Plant Materials Held in the Kew Economic Botany Collection

U	O	R	S	A	M	K	S	B	L	U	B	A	D	O
D	I	A	T	N	E	H	R	S	N	I	S	E	R	E
E	L	T	I	E	M	R	T	A	P	I	R	D	C	L
W	S	C	U	S	G	I	I	O	B	H	Y	I	O	E
X	E	E	R	U	G	X	L	A	I	M	U	S	M	A
T	E	N	F	M	B	L	S	Z	L	J	E	M	D	F
Y	D	T	A	X	E	T	O	O	F	R	N	T	I	B
S	S	S	A	N	O	M	E	A	O	N	O	L	S	U
N	O	D	U	L	E	S	E	P	S	F	Y	O	J	D
W	S	C	O	S	N	L	S	S	P	M	F	C	T	S
E	O	N	C	E	H	S	O	E	O	A	R	I	L	S
I	S	O	M	H	E	H	T	V	A	T	R	O	G	Y
S	T	A	D	A	I	O	E	A	F	R	U	N	C	R
T	T	E	C	N	E	C	S	E	R	O	L	F	N	I
S	R	E	B	U	T	S	L	L	A	G	F	A	E	L

◊ AERIAL ROOTS
◊ ARILS
◊ BULBS
◊ CORMS
◊ FRUITS
◊ INFLORESCENCE
◊ LATEX
◊ LEAF BUDS
◊ LEAF GALLS
◊ LEAF JUICE
◊ LEAVES
◊ NECTAR
◊ NODULES
◊ OIL SEEDS
◊ POLLEN
◊ RESIN
◊ RHIZOMES
◊ SPORES
◊ STAMENS
◊ STEM BARK
◊ STIGMAS
◊ STOLONS
◊ TUBERS
◊ WOOD

Flora of the Alps

◊ *ACHILLEA ATRATA*

◊ *ACONITUM NAPELLUS*

◊ *ALCHEMILLA ALPINA*

◊ *ASPHODELUS ALBUS*

◊ *CALTHA PALUSTRIS*

◊ *CAMPANULA PERSICIFOLIA*

◊ *CROCUS VERNUS*

◊ *DIANTHUS PAVONIUS*

◊ *DIGITALIS LUTEA*

◊ *DRYAS OCTOPETALA*

◊ *ERITRICHIUM NANUM*

◊ *GENTIANA ACAULIS*

◊ *GEUM MONTANUM*

◊ *LILIUM BULBIFERUM*

◊ *NIGRITELLA RHELLICANI*

◊ *PHYTEUMA SPICATUM*

◊ *RANUNCULUS GLACIALIS*

◊ *RUMEX NIVALIS*

◊ *SAXIFRAGA OPPOSITIFOLIA*

◊ *SENECIO OVATUS*

◊ *SILENE VULGARIS*

◊ *TRIFOLIUM ALPINUM*

◊ *TROLLIUS EUROPAEUS*

◊ *VERATRUM ALBUM*

55 Trees of Europe (Common Names)

- ◊ ASPEN
- ◊ BLACK POPLAR
- ◊ CRACK WILLOW
- ◊ CRETAN DATE PALM
- ◊ FALSE MEDLAR
- ◊ FIELD MAPLE
- ◊ FOETID JUNIPER
- ◊ FRENCH TAMARISK
- ◊ GREEK FIR
- ◊ LOCK ELM
- ◊ MARITIME PINE
- ◊ MEDITERRANEAN CYPRESS
- ◊ MIDLAND HAWTHORN
- ◊ NORWAY SPRUCE
- ◊ OLD WORLD SYCAMORE
- ◊ OLIVE
- ◊ ONE-LEAVED ASH
- ◊ SICILIAN FIR
- ◊ SPECKLED ALDER
- ◊ STRANDZHA OAK
- ◊ SYCAMORE MAPLE
- ◊ VITEX
- ◊ WYCH ELM
- ◊ YEW

56 Songs with Plants and Flowers in the Title

W	E	A	R	B	B	E	S	O	R	C	H	F	Y	H
M	I	W	E	S	U	O	X	L	I	P	D	S	S	I
S	U	L	B	E	Y	T	J	N	B	S	I	C	E	B
H	A	Y	D	I	L	X	T	E	J	A	H	A	I	I
A	N	A	P	F	I	B	D	E	D	V	C	L	S	H
R	R	R	S	X	L	O	M	C	R	G	R	I	I	A
O	O	G	B	S	F	O	S	A	C	C	O	L	A	I
N	H	H	Y	P	I	W	W	W	R	A	U	G	D	L
T	T	Y	F	V	C	E	I	E	K	B	B	P	R	O
E	O	A	B	C	V	L	W	T	R	I	T	E	E	N
H	K	C	T	L	L	I	R	L	R	S	D	A	A	G
E	K	I	L	O	A	E	O	C	E	I	T	S	M	A
S	I	N	W	G	E	C	H	L	R	D	H	A	I	M
A	N	T	N	U	L	M	K	I	E	M	E	M	N	E
P	G	H	O	I	K	I	S	A	A	T	U	A	G	R

- ◊ *BED OF ROSES*
- ◊ *BIRCH TREE*
- ◊ *BLACK ROSE*
- ◊ *BLUE ORCHID*
- ◊ *BRAMBLE ROSE*
- ◊ *BUILD ME UP BUTTERCUP*
- ◊ *DAISY LANE*
- ◊ *EDELWEISS*
- ◊ *EVERY ROSE HAS ITS THORN*
- ◊ *FAKE PLASTIC TREES*
- ◊ *HYACINTH HOUSE*
- ◊ *IRIS*
- ◊ *KING OF TREES*
- ◊ *LA VIE EN ROSE*
- ◊ *LILAC WINE*
- ◊ *LILY OF THE WEST*
- ◊ *MIGHTY OAK TREE*
- ◊ *PSYCHO DAISIES*
- ◊ *ROSE OF SHARON*
- ◊ *SUGAR MAGNOLIA*
- ◊ *THE DREAMING TREE*
- ◊ *VIOLET HILL*
- ◊ *WEEPING WILLOW*
- ◊ *WILDFLOWERS*

57 Plant-Derived Boys' Names

```
E L Y I L N N Y T S O M T O L
R A R Y E L I A R A V I N D O
E A G D H S E A F P H I L A Y
V A N J A S F W M B Y A H M H
I I G L F O J L M H A R E E D
L D D I R A Y F O A Y H A S N
O E K E C A J E M R R W T T O
R L S I N O H N L F I B H R T
A T N H J A R V I D A A E Y N
E T Y S A W H A L S A D N A R
O E O H R E T G I A N E S L O
E E V O E S Y L O A N V H C H
Y I W L D L D H E E A U Y R T
E A F A R E M L O D R A K A B
N F L I N F O R D A N E P B R
```

◊ ALDER
◊ ARAVIND
◊ ARVID
◊ BARCLAY
◊ BASIL
◊ BRAMWELL
◊ EOGHAN
◊ FLORIAN
◊ FOREST
◊ HEADLEY
◊ HEATH
◊ JACEK
◊ JACINTO
◊ JARED
◊ KUNAL
◊ LINDEN
◊ LINFORD
◊ MOSTYN
◊ OLEANDER
◊ OLIVER
◊ REED
◊ ROWAN
◊ TERHO
◊ THORNTON

Genera in the Family: Myrtaceae – Part Two (Myrtle Family)

◊ *AMOMYRTELLA*

◊ *ANGOPHORA*

◊ *BAECKEA*

◊ *CALYTRIX*

◊ *CLOEZIA*

◊ *EUCALYPTOPSIS*

◊ *EURYOMYRTUS*

◊ *HOTTEA*

◊ *KANIA*

◊ *KUNZEA*

◊ *LENWEBBIA*

◊ *LOPHOMYRTUS*

◊ *MELALEUCA*

◊ *MOSIERA*

◊ *MYRCIA*

◊ *PSIDIUM*

◊ *RHODAMNIA*

◊ *TAXANDRIA*

◊ *UROMYRTUS*

◊ *WATERHOUSEA*

59 Economically Important Plants

O	E	R	S	C	G	R	E	S	S	P	A	G	Y	S
A	D	N	F	S	P	Y	H	D	U	I	H	R	F	I
T	A	C	E	E	A	T	B	O	S	N	R	J	O	E
C	I	T	P	J	E	R	N	Y	R	E	L	E	C	R
I	L	P	C	L	I	I	G	I	B	C	D	E	S	A
T	E	E	M	U	G	E	L	P	M	C	H	G	E	L
R	M	A	E	A	G	O	A	C	R	E	S	I	E	L
U	O	R	S	E	Y	O	U	U	O	L	I	O	D	I
S	R	N	S	P	S	X	C	R	M	F	H	L	N	D
N	B	O	P	O	U	I	U	M	D	A	F	L	D	O
R	R	O	F	R	F	R	D	J	Y	Y	L	E	J	P
O	P	I	T	E	D	Y	G	C	P	R	A	L	E	A
E	L	E	R	U	A	L	C	E	A	H	T	M	O	S
U	W	E	H	S	A	C	R	A	L	H	I	L	L	W
M	A	H	O	G	A	N	Y	E	M	I	N	A	E	E

◊ BROMELIAD
◊ CASHEW
◊ CELERY
◊ CITRUS
◊ COFFEE
◊ CRUCIFER
◊ GOURD
◊ GRASS
◊ LAUREL
◊ LEGUME
◊ MAHOGANY
◊ MALLOW
◊ MINT
◊ MYRTLE
◊ ORCHID
◊ PALM
◊ PEPPER
◊ PINE
◊ POPPY
◊ ROSE
◊ SAPODILLA
◊ SEDGE
◊ SOAPBERRY
◊ SPURGE

60 Individual Trees of Note – Historic

◊ ANNE FRANK TREE
◊ BEAMAN OAK
◊ BURMIS TREE
◊ CHANGI TREE
◊ CHAPMAN'S BAOBAB
◊ CYPRESS OF KASHMAR
◊ EISENHOWER TREE
◊ ENCINO OAK TREE
◊ GLASTONBURY THORN
◊ GREAT ELM
◊ HERBIE
◊ HOOKER OAK
◊ LINCOLN OAK
◊ LONE PINE
◊ MERLIN'S OAK
◊ MINGO OAK
◊ MOTHER OF THE FOREST
◊ OLD GUM TREE
◊ PANKE BAOBAB
◊ PROMETHEUS
◊ SEPARATION TREE
◊ THE BODHI TREE
◊ THE SENATOR
◊ THOR'S OAK

61 Excerpt – *Kew Gardens* (1921) by Virginia Woolf

From the oval-shaped flower-bed there rose perhaps a hundred stalks spreading into heart-shaped or tongue-shaped leaves half way up and unfurling at the tip red or blue or yellow petals marked with spots of colour raised upon the surface; and from the red, blue or yellow gloom of the throat emerged a straight bar, rough with gold dust and slightly clubbed at the end. The petals were voluminous enough to be stirred by the summer breeze, and when they moved, the red, blue and yellow lights passed one over the other, staining an inch of the brown earth beneath with a spot of the most intricate colour. The light fell either upon the smooth, grey back of a pebble, or, the shell of a snail with its brown, circular veins, or falling into a raindrop, it expanded with such intensity of red, blue and yellow the thin walls of water that one expected them to burst and disappear. Instead, the drop was left in a second silver grey once more, and the light now settled upon the flesh of a leaf, revealing the branching thread of fibre beneath the surface, and again it moved on and spread its illumination in the vast green spaces beneath the dome of the heart-shaped and tongue-shaped leaves. Then the breeze stirred rather more briskly overhead and the colour was flashed into the air above, into the eyes of the men and women who walk in Kew Gardens in July.

R A E Y T I S N E T N I C N S
A G A W A Y K P H E H C N I U
I A R G L E L C O U R G D H R
S R T N E L S U A T N E I T F
E D H I A L E N J B P D I L A
D E U L B O V F R A P N R D C
W N E R S W A E H E T E B E E
H S O U E O E S T R V R S T D
O W R F Y Z L A I L I E P C A
N A D N E A L C I S C O R E E
B T O U V S A S K O N S E P L
P S M O O T H L N O N B A X B
O A E W E K Y D W A L K D E B
R V M E G N I N I A T S U D E
D E H S A L F L S T A L K S P

62 Genera in the Family: Orchidaceae – Part Three (Orchid Family)

D	I	P	E	J	A	R	O	R	P	O	L	P	I	D
U	A	C	Y	R	T	O	C	H	I	L	U	M	X	A
C	L	L	Y	P	E	R	A	N	T	H	U	S	A	S
Y	L	A	B	R	N	O	D	E	T	I	P	I	T	E
N	E	I	E	O	I	P	I	X	G	U	R	E	C	R
U	E	D	L	M	C	E	A	O	E	E	R	A	R	R
T	D	E	O	E	A	F	P	U	M	E	L	M	Y	I
H	E	I	G	N	R	I	M	O	O	A	V	E	P	M
E	I	W	L	A	P	O	N	C	N	D	H	S	T	A
L	H	U	O	E	V	O	H	T	H	U	W	I	O	C
A	C	E	T	A	M	I	H	N	M	E	D	E	P	O
S	S	N	T	J	L	E	L	I	A	V	E	L	Y	L
I	Y	P	I	U	K	E	G	E	L	I	E	L	L	A
S	T	B	S	C	S	O	B	R	A	L	I	A	O	L
N	E	O	M	O	O	R	E	A	P	I	A	U	S	U

- ◊ *ACINETA*
- ◊ *AMESIELLA*
- ◊ *BELOGLOTTIS*
- ◊ *CALANTHE*
- ◊ *CRYPTOPYLOS*
- ◊ *CYRTOCHILUM*
- ◊ *DIPLOPRORA*
- ◊ *EPIPOGIUM*
- ◊ *GAVILEA*
- ◊ *KEGELIELLA*
- ◊ *LYPERANTHUS*
- ◊ *MONOMERIA*
- ◊ *NEOMOOREA*
- ◊ *NEUWIEDIA*
- ◊ *PROMENAEA*
- ◊ *RIMACOLA*
- ◊ *SCHIEDEELLA*
- ◊ *SOBRALIA*
- ◊ *STEREOCHILUS*
- ◊ *THELASIS*

63 National Trees (Common Names)

E	B	E	B	A	N	Y	O	S	B	M	E	N	E	W
G	E	J	N	O	Y	R	S	O	C	E	A	I	Y	I
E	E	T	L	I	H	B	A	B	O	A	B	N	R	W
A	R	Y	S	U	N	O	R	O	W	J	U	N	G	M
R	E	B	R	A	Z	I	L	W	O	O	D	E	D	O
C	P	U	N	E	C	D	U	P	U	O	E	D	E	N
E	H	S	D	C	R	A	U	Q	U	G	L	L	O	K
V	F	A	I	S	Y	A	N	B	Y	C	I	O	D	E
I	U	T	B	B	G	C	H	A	E	N	S	G	A	Y
L	L	T	H	G	E	U	L	H	U	T	S	F	R	O
O	B	I	E	C	T	R	P	D	L	G	E	S	Y	E
M	Y	D	E	A	L	V	I	O	M	J	S	A	M	A
E	P	A	N	A	M	A	Y	A	K	M	A	P	L	E
W	H	I	T	E	W	O	O	D	N	O	H	R	A	E
P	G	N	E	D	N	I	L	D	E	L	K	Y	P	A

- ◊ BAOBAB (MADAGASCAR)
- ◊ BHUTAN CYPRESS (BHUTAN)
- ◊ BRAZILWOOD (BRAZIL)
- ◊ CEIBO (ARGENTINA)
- ◊ CEYLON IRONWOOD (SRI LANKA)
- ◊ DEODAR CEDAR (PAKISTAN)
- ◊ GOLDEN WATTLE (AUSTRALIA)
- ◊ GUANACASTE (COSTA RICA)
- ◊ LINDEN (SLOVENIA)
- ◊ MANGO TREE (BANGLADESH)
- ◊ MAPLE (CANADA)
- ◊ MONKEY PUZZLE (CHILE)
- ◊ OLIVE TREE (ALBANIA)
- ◊ PALMYRA PALM (CAMBODIA)
- ◊ PANAMA TREE (REPUBLIC OF PANAMA)
- ◊ POKOK MERBAU (MALAYSIA)
- ◊ QUININE TREE (PERU)
- ◊ SESSILE OAK (IRELAND)
- ◊ SIBERIAN FIR (RUSSIA)
- ◊ WHITEWOOD (ANTIGUA AND BARBUDA)

Plants of the Himalayas

A	I	N	U	H	A	P	W	R	A	M	M	E	A	M
M	U	N	I	M	S	A	J	U	R	U	P	E	A	U
O	C	A	R	S	U	C	S	R	T	M	C	E	R	I
O	U	R	L	J	A	E	M	N	S	E	A	L	A	L
C	Y	E	H	L	M	U	A	U	G	H	L	L	N	I
O	C	M	T	O	I	I	L	S	R	T	U	J	E	L
L	G	H	S	C	D	U	U	U	E	N	M	F	M	A
Q	A	E	Y	A	C	O	M	R	I	A	I	A	O	N
U	A	L	R	S	E	H	D	D	P	I	R	L	N	I
H	E	C	E	A	U	R	I	E	I	A	P	U	E	D
O	C	A	N	I	N	H	O	C	N	M	O	T	F	N
U	I	A	V	A	M	I	G	H	U	D	R	E	S	A
N	P	A	N	D	A	N	U	S	S	O	R	B	P	N
I	L	B	Y	E	B	A	B	M	S	D	M	O	S	A
A	G	A	P	E	T	E	S	A	W	A	N	U	N	R

- ◊ *ADIANTUM VENUSTUM*
- ◊ *AESCULUS INDICA*
- ◊ *AGAPETES SERPENS*
- ◊ *ALLIUM WALLICHII*
- ◊ *ANEMONE VITIFOLIA*
- ◊ *BETULA UTILIS*
- ◊ *CALTHA PALUSTRIS*
- ◊ *CEDRUS DEODARA*
- ◊ *COLQUHOUNIA VESTITA*
- ◊ *GERANIUM WALLICHIANUM*
- ◊ *INULA HOOKERI*
- ◊ *JASMINUM PARKERI*
- ◊ *LILIUM NEPALENSE*
- ◊ *LYCIUM BARBARUM*
- ◊ *MAIANTHEMUM OLERACEUM*
- ◊ *MESUA FERREA*
- ◊ *NANDINA DOMESTICA*
- ◊ *PANDANUS FURCATUS*
- ◊ *PICEA SMITHIANA*
- ◊ *PINUS ROXBURGHII*
- ◊ *PRIMULA DENTICULATA*
- ◊ *RHODODENDRON ARBOREUM*
- ◊ *ROSA BRUNONII*
- ◊ *SHOREA ROBUSTA*

65 Famous Botanists – Part Two

```
M A N Y B T S E N O T X A P E
E N I Y E E M U J S E F L E R
R N O W T R G B I W E S O N E
I O S S V R R I P S A B E Y S
O S R R L O A O W R U N I V H
I N J E H I U M T D U L O B C
Y A E I M G W H B T E T C W U
E D I B A I U N R T R H L S F
L A D E R R N O C E R L H E S
D L E N T U F I L B A U H I N
N A V E R D N G P T F N H R E
I V R S A C N F T L P U A F O
L E I W B E O U E E A A L C D
A S E E I G N D C L P R E S O
M R S F A N E A M H S B S C D
```

- ◊ MICHEL ADANSON
- ◊ PROSPERO ALPINI
- ◊ JOSEPH CHARLES ARTHUR
- ◊ JOHN BARTRAM
- ◊ GASPARD BAUHIN
- ◊ EMMA LUCY BRAUN
- ◊ OTTO BRUNFELS
- ◊ CAROLUS CLUSIUS
- ◊ CHARLES DARWIN
- ◊ HUGO DE VRIES
- ◊ REMBERT DODOENS
- ◊ ADOLF ENGLER
- ◊ ROBERT FORTUNE
- ◊ ELIAS FRIES
- ◊ LEONHARD FUCHS
- ◊ STEPHEN HALES
- ◊ JOHANN HEDWIG
- ◊ JOHN LINDLEY
- ◊ JOHANNES MARTYN
- ◊ THOMAS NUTTALL
- ◊ JOSEPH PAXTON
- ◊ JEAN SENEBIER
- ◊ JOHN TORREY
- ◊ ERNEST HENRY WILSON

66 Houseplants (Common Names)

S	O	R	R	U	B	E	R	N	A	C	A	W	C	N
K	A	L	A	N	C	H	O	E	H	H	A	W	A	N
F	L	E	R	A	S	R	P	I	B	N	D	C	S	X
R	A	S	T	C	L	U	N	R	A	B	I	R	T	A
S	X	E	A	P	O	E	G	I	E	R	U	R	I	R
Y	A	A	L	T	S	R	U	A	F	D	O	R	R	R
H	L	M	R	E	I	G	A	A	R	Y	I	M	O	O
G	S	I	T	X	L	N	H	L	P	A	A	P	N	W
R	Y	I	L	S	E	D	A	J	B	R	P	S	S	H
A	S	A	L	E	I	A	D	A	A	E	A	S	N	E
P	C	I	D	G	C	R	O	I	C	R	A	Y	A	A
E	I	U	T	E	N	A	H	U	F	C	E	D	E	D
I	F	R	R	U	D	E	E	C	U	N	U	A	G	R
V	I	A	P	E	W	E	E	P	I	N	G	Y	A	R
Y	C	R	O	W	N	O	F	T	H	O	R	N	S	I

◊ AFRICAN VIOLET
◊ ARECA PALM
◊ ARROWHEAD VINE
◊ ASPARAGUS FERN
◊ BURRO'S TAIL
◊ CAST IRON PLANT
◊ CHINESE MONEY PLANT
◊ CHRISTMAS CACTUS
◊ CORAL BEAD
◊ CROWN OF THORNS
◊ ENGLISH IVY
◊ FIDDLE LEAF FIG
◊ GRAPE IVY
◊ GUIANA CHESTNUT
◊ JADE PLANT
◊ KALANCHOE
◊ PEACE LILY
◊ PRAYER PLANT
◊ RUBBER FIG
◊ SATIN POTHOS
◊ SPIDER PLANT
◊ WAX PLANT
◊ WEEPING FIG
◊ YUCCA

67 Extinct Prehistoric Plant Species and Genera – Part Two

M	D	R	O	S	E	R	A	P	I	T	E	S	C	E
A	O	F	U	N	T	C	O	R	N	U	S	A	O	S
L	M	X	S	A	L	L	O	Z	A	E	Y	V	E	N
A	A	R	I	N	A	M	R	E	T	T	E	D	V	E
T	P	D	E	J	T	T	I	I	O	U	U	N	Y	K
A	A	I	U	P	R	E	A	N	N	A	B	I	E	S
N	N	N	H	X	S	D	I	L	L	I	W	H	S	A
I	N	W	O	U	R	A	N	R	O	S	A	X	C	L
T	A	O	O	O	L	F	I	U	A	R	M	R	H	A
E	U	R	C	E	E	T	A	D	H	V	T	V	T	P
S	L	B	S	A	I	E	M	O	R	U	E	L	P	L
O	I	C	H	A	N	E	Y	I	B	A	I	E	R	A
N	K	S	T	E	W	A	R	T	I	E	K	D	I	A
P	A	G	I	O	P	H	Y	L	L	U	M	C	A	E
I	V	Y	A	I	N	O	S	M	A	I	L	L	I	W

- ◊ *ABIES MILLERI*
- ◊ *ACER ALASKENSE*
- ◊ *ACER ASHWILLI*
- ◊ *ACER BROWNI*
- ◊ *ACER CHANEYI*
- ◊ *ACER DETTERMANI*
- ◊ *ACER ROUSEI*
- ◊ *ACER STEWARTI*
- ◊ *ACER TRAINI*
- ◊ *AZOLLA PRIMAEVA*
- ◊ *BAIERA*
- ◊ *CAYTONIALES*
- ◊ *CORDAITES*
- ◊ *CORNUS PIGGAE*
- ◊ *DROSERAPITES*
- ◊ *KARDIASPERMA*
- ◊ *LATANITES*
- ◊ *PAGIOPHYLLUM*
- ◊ *PANNAULIKA*
- ◊ *PLEUROMEIA*
- ◊ *TAXUS MASONII*
- ◊ *WILLIAMSONIA*

68 Plants Painted in Australasia – Marianne North Collection at Kew

S	A	P	O	C	Y	N	E	A	S	D	T	A	F	B
I	A	I	S	K	N	A	B	U	R	T	O	N	I	A
L	I	F	A	M	E	E	T	S	I	S	E	E	V	M
B	U	E	R	L	U	O	I	A	V	E	U	D	S	R
Y	O	B	E	M	N	I	C	T	S	T	C	N	U	E
B	E	M	H	I	U	A	R	U	N	A	A	E	H	P
N	I	B	T	P	C	I	T	E	I	T	L	L	T	S
P	U	C	N	I	F	O	N	R	C	A	Y	L	N	E
S	A	Y	A	J	N	A	A	E	E	Y	P	E	A	M
U	R	I	T	A	C	E	M	T	L	E	T	B	R	O
B	I	V	S	S	L	R	R	O	N	P	U	A	O	C
U	C	Y	O	O	I	O	H	N	T	S	S	H	L	Y
R	H	E	R	A	P	A	T	E	C	O	M	A	Y	P
T	E	U	P	A	Y	C	S	U	N	A	S	U	F	H
F	A	A	L	S	O	P	H	I	L	A	N	I	A	I

- ◊ *ACACIA ALATA*
- ◊ *ACTINOTUS HELIANTHI*
- ◊ *ALSOPHILA AUSTRALIS*
- ◊ *APOCYNEA*
- ◊ *ASPLENIUM NIDUS*
- ◊ *BANKSIA GRANDIS*
- ◊ *BELLENDENA MONTANA*
- ◊ *BURTONIA CONFERTA*
- ◊ *BYBLIS GIGANTEA*
- ◊ *COMESPERMA*
- ◊ *EUCALYPTUS GLOBULUS*
- ◊ *FUSANUS SPICATUS*
- ◊ *ISOTOMA BROWNI*
- ◊ *LAPORTEA MOROIDES*
- ◊ *LORANTHUS PENDULUS*
- ◊ *NUYTSIA FLORIBUNDA*
- ◊ *OLEARIA ARGOPHYLLA*
- ◊ *PIMELEA*
- ◊ *PLATYCERIUM GRANDE*
- ◊ *PROSTANTHERA*
- ◊ *RICHEA DRACOPHYLLA*
- ◊ *RUBUS AUSTRALIS*
- ◊ *TECOMA AUSTRALIS*
- ◊ *THYSANOTUS*

69 Buildings and Features of Kew

H L O Y E V I S E R A R S I L

S V R P W S S A W D E U A O R

A H A F A I E D K L A S C M Y

N L N E T N V N K A H V H T E

M T G F E Y O C A I A C I R H

Y S E N R H A L R P R M T E D

I O R S L S I L L A A M U E S

C P Y U I J E X D E R J T T F

E M C L L Y D E T A B Y R O A

H O A O Y B N C A D O G A P K

O C M E V I H E H T R G E V N

U L R A U P A L A C E T F O I

S C A R E T H U S A T V A I M

E T S N E E N O I T U L O V E

I A S N O B L E I M M E S V L

◊ AGIUS EVOLUTION GARDEN

◊ BONSAI HOUSE

◊ COMPOST HEAP

◊ ICE HOUSE

◊ JAPANESE GATEWAY

◊ KEW PALACE

◊ MINKA HOUSE

◊ NASH CONSERVATORY

◊ ORANGERY

◊ PAGODA

◊ PALM HOUSE

◊ SACKLER CROSSING

◊ SHIRLEY SHERWOOD GALLERY

◊ TEMPLE OF AEOLUS

◊ TEMPLE OF ARETHUSA

◊ TEMPLE OF BELLONA

◊ THE ARBORETUM

◊ THE DAVIES ALPINE HOUSE

◊ THE HIVE

◊ THE RUINED ARCH

◊ TREETOP WALKWAY

◊ WATERLILY HOUSE

70 Palms – Part One (Common Names)

```
S A B E D L N A I R A D I B U
A M A U G A R I M F W H I T E
L P Z E T N X H C S L U Y P W
A T B O T T L E T E H A V O I
F V N L M U E H N I G K H I N
R U I A H B G R M B N I I Y D
I M B S G I I A F Y T N U O M
C A Y H W E L E E L N A H C I
A N C N D A L C B P Y I J T L
N I C O Y U R E M I A M P C L
D L C A R A N D A Y A C O S T
E A N U R U I A N G P N A L A
A S Y I A N R E A I N C T Y R
N E E D L E N U M B R E L L A
J A W C A E P U L A D A U G W
```

- ◊ AFRICAN OIL PALM
- ◊ ANDEAN WAX PALM
- ◊ BOTTLE PALM
- ◊ BUTTERFLY PALM
- ◊ CARANDAY WAX PALM
- ◊ COYURE PALM
- ◊ DARIAN PALM
- ◊ ELEGANT PALM
- ◊ GUADALUPE PALM
- ◊ HIMALAYAN PINANGA
- ◊ MANAMBE PALM
- ◊ MANILA PALM
- ◊ MIRAGUAMA PALM
- ◊ MOUNT LEWIS KING PALM
- ◊ NEEDLE PALM
- ◊ NIKAU PALM
- ◊ PACAYA PALM
- ◊ SPINY LICUALA PALM
- ◊ TARAW PALM
- ◊ UMBRELLA PALM
- ◊ WHITE BACKED PALM
- ◊ WIGHT'S SAGO PALM
- ◊ WINDMILL PALM
- ◊ ZOMBIE PALM

71

Only-Known Species in the Genera – Part One (Common Names)

A	I	X	S	S	O	M	Y	T	U	O	G	M	E	A
S	S	O	M	G	A	L	F	L	A	R	O	S	P	R
A	L	E	X	A	N	D	R	I	A	N	L	R	J	G
S	U	N	E	V	K	E	O	W	A	A	S	L	A	E
L	E	H	P	M	D	A	G	V	F	E	M	C	J	K
Y	S	A	L	D	A	F	N	M	E	G	I	A	N	T
A	E	S	V	N	N	N	F	A	A	T	I	F	N	R
L	N	O	J	A	S	A	Y	L	W	M	R	O	G	N
L	I	F	G	B	F	A	L	S	I	A	M	E	F	O
I	H	L	O	O	H	I	E	S	E	A	O	O	E	D
A	C	Y	B	J	T	C	H	Y	N	E	I	M	A	O
A	N	I	L	O	R	A	C	N	E	E	D	E	N	T
T	X	S	I	J	S	B	I	A	R	Y	E	M	C	S
L	A	H	N	D	S	C	S	R	N	N	O	U	H	A
W	C	Y	H	S	U	R	B	H	C	E	E	L	Q	M

◊ ALEXANDRIAN LAUREL
◊ CAROLINA REDROOT
◊ CHINESE THUJA
◊ CHIOTILLA
◊ CINNAMON FERN
◊ DOVE-TREE
◊ FALSE UNICORN
◊ FLAG-MOSS
◊ FLY POISON
◊ GIANT FORGET-ME-NOT
◊ GOBLIN GOLD
◊ GOUTY-MOSS
◊ HUON PINE
◊ JOJOBA
◊ KANAWAO
◊ KAROO ROSE
◊ LEECHBRUSH
◊ LYALLIA CUSHION
◊ MANYSEED GOOSEFOOT
◊ MASTODON PALM
◊ OAT SPEARGRASS
◊ QUEENSLAND KENTIA
◊ SAW PALMETTO
◊ VENUS FLYTRAP

Forests and Woods of the UK

E	Y	V	Y	B	R	E	C	H	F	A	T	X	U	E
S	V	E	B	E	A	E	B	E	Y	C	D	B	N	S
A	Y	B	L	I	S	A	B	T	A	A	C	E	K	L
L	E	B	A	N	V	Y	W	M	S	B	W	C	E	D
C	P	I	D	S	I	Y	W	H	A	F	U	I	W	O
E	P	R	Y	A	C	W	D	N	O	P	G	R	H	N
Y	I	Y	G	H	B	O	S	R	R	H	A	F	I	O
A	N	I	W	Y	W	X	E	U	E	R	W	F	T	D
M	G	O	R	N	S	S	J	N	D	I	I	A	E	L
S	O	W	H	A	T	F	I	E	L	D	E	N	L	A
D	G	S	Y	F	I	N	G	L	E	C	N	E	E	H
E	M	N	X	D	J	U	S	A	I	C	W	L	A	D
W	E	G	I	O	Y	J	E	L	K	Y	A	G	F	E
E	I	V	H	K	S	R	B	U	R	N	H	A	M	L
B	A	N	A	G	H	E	R	E	M	A	L	E	D	L

- ◊ ASHDOWN FOREST
- ◊ BADBY WOOD
- ◊ BANAGHER GLEN
- ◊ BRECHFA FOREST
- ◊ BURNHAM BEECHES
- ◊ DALBY FOREST
- ◊ DELAMERE FOREST
- ◊ EPPING FOREST
- ◊ FINGLE WOODS
- ◊ GLEN AFFRIC
- ◊ GWYDYR FOREST
- ◊ HALDON FOREST
- ◊ HATFIELD FOREST
- ◊ KIELDER FOREST
- ◊ KING'S WOOD
- ◊ LEIGH WOODS
- ◊ NEW FOREST
- ◊ PAMBER FOREST
- ◊ PUCK'S GLEN
- ◊ SALCEY FOREST
- ◊ SWINLEY FOREST
- ◊ WHITELEAF HILL
- ◊ WYCHWOOD
- ◊ WYRE FOREST

Palms – Part Two (Common Names)

B	B	I	S	M	A	R	C	K	N	L	A	D	Y	Y
M	A	J	E	S	T	I	C	O	S	T	L	W	U	L
H	Y	M	A	C	A	R	T	H	U	R	I	A	T	L
E	L	V	E	Y	A	R	E	N	Y	I	P	R	U	E
C	V	O	L	R	E	R	L	A	E	X	S	F	N	J
A	I	N	U	H	I	E	O	T	N	K	T	F	O	D
R	Y	L	T	L	T	A	A	L	V	E	I	A	C	R
O	S	A	L	E	U	O	T	C	I	C	C	N	O	Y
H	A	H	B	A	C	H	R	I	D	N	K	N	C	A
C	O	B	S	I	T	T	I	E	L	V	A	W	H	I
O	S	O	T	T	R	E	H	W	G	O	S	A	G	O
H	U	T	P	I	I	W	M	X	A	N	S	S	E	H
C	E	R	A	E	B	Y	D	D	E	T	I	D	S	E
P	S	U	G	A	R	A	L	F	O	T	A	F	R	D
X	F	O	R	M	O	S	A	I	R	A	Z	A	M	A

- ◊ ATHERTON PALM
- ◊ BETEL NUT PALM
- ◊ BISMARCK PALM
- ◊ CAROLINA PALMETTO
- ◊ CHOCHO PALM
- ◊ COCONUT PALM
- ◊ DWARF FAN PALM
- ◊ FINGER PALM
- ◊ FORMOSA PALM
- ◊ HOOPER'S PALM
- ◊ JELLY PALM
- ◊ KENTIA PALM
- ◊ LADY PALM
- ◊ LIPSTICK PALM
- ◊ LO'ULU HIWA PALM
- ◊ MACARTHUR PALM
- ◊ MAJESTIC PALM
- ◊ MAZARI PALM
- ◊ METALLIC PALM
- ◊ PETTICOAT PALM
- ◊ SAGO PALM
- ◊ SOLITAIRE PALM
- ◊ SUGAR PALM
- ◊ TEDDY BEAR PALM

Herbs and Medicinal Herbs

V	E	E	B	A	Y	L	E	A	F	L	V	E	R	A
O	N	A	G	E	R	O	W	C	G	I	Y	H	B	S
U	S	H	S	A	V	N	H	O	R	V	A	U	T	E
E	O	E	H	U	R	A	N	I	B	R	X	J	C	R
L	R	H	E	B	M	O	Y	S	N	E	O	H	R	O
T	R	Y	L	O	C	L	B	G	C	H	I	V	E	S
T	E	U	M	A	C	D	I	O	N	C	R	L	D	S
E	L	I	F	I	O	H	R	S	O	H	L	U	N	O
N	L	E	L	Y	P	I	W	R	A	I	I	R	E	N
E	I	R	N	B	A	O	Y	B	D	B	F	G	V	I
S	A	T	M	N	R	O	E	C	A	R	A	W	A	Y
G	U	I	D	T	E	M	Y	H	T	S	P	Y	L	V
L	N	E	T	N	I	F	B	U	R	D	O	C	K	A
T	R	N	E	D	N	Y	E	L	S	R	A	P	A	E
U	H	O	L	S	S	A	R	G	N	O	M	E	L	O

◊ BASIL
◊ BAY LEAF
◊ BORAGE
◊ BURDOCK
◊ CARAWAY
◊ CHAMOMILE
◊ CHERVIL
◊ CHICORY
◊ CHIVES
◊ CORIANDER
◊ DILL
◊ FENNEL
◊ GARLIC
◊ LAVENDER
◊ LEMONGRASS
◊ MINT
◊ NETTLE
◊ OREGANO
◊ PARSLEY
◊ RUE
◊ SAGE
◊ SORREL
◊ ST. JOHN'S WORT
◊ THYME

75 Shrubs – Part One (Common Names)

A I T N O M E R F Y E A M M Y
A I S H C U F N B E I I E X R
A I R W S V P B H L G S V V R
C E G V U U U P L P O B I Y E
A S L N Y R R E B R A B R O B
R S D A H B M B K A U D G V W
A A A S Z A N C E R E A I D O
G G O P C A O A N L S I N O N
P E V V A R R U C V T Z I G S
O B I C V I M A Y I Y T A H E
S R C Y P E B H E G X U O O W
S U B S H Y D R A N G E A B E
Y S M O K E T R E E Y D M B S
H H W U X K R A B E N I N L R
F R I N G E T R E E C W I E O

- ◊ AZALEA
- ◊ BARBERRY
- ◊ BOTTLEBRUSH
- ◊ BOX
- ◊ CAMELLIA
- ◊ DAPHNE
- ◊ DEUTZIA
- ◊ DOGHOBBLE
- ◊ FREMONTIA
- ◊ FRINGETREE
- ◊ FUCHSIA
- ◊ HYDRANGEA
- ◊ HYSSOP
- ◊ MEXICAN BUCKEYE
- ◊ NINEBARK
- ◊ ROCK-ROSE
- ◊ SAGEBRUSH
- ◊ SHRUBBY VERONICA
- ◊ SMOKETREE
- ◊ SNOWBERRY
- ◊ SPIRAEA
- ◊ VIBURNUM
- ◊ VIRGINIA SWEETSPIRE
- ◊ YUCCA

76 Plants and Flowers in Film Titles

```
T F V F R O L R E D N E V A L
U R T R R I F I R M R U W F W
L D I C T Y E V F E V I L O G
P E H F O R R E O E T O S N X
A I A F F A N O E L W P E X M
D E E F G I Y R E E S K E A A
W O N S M X D O R E O D R C G
P H W S M D M S E R A I T C N
W S A L U D W E B H G W Y A O
I J E D W R A S L O F U R C L
L A Y N A V E I L B E B U T I
L H U S I I A D S F H O N U A
O V H Y N P S O N I I P A S S
W B O R E H R Y U U E R O C B
S M S Y R A M E S O R S B E N
```

◊ *A NEW LEAF*
◊ *A NIGHTMARE ON ELM STREET*
◊ *BLUE JASMINE*
◊ *BROKEN FLOWERS*
◊ *CACTUS FLOWER*
◊ *DRIVING MISS DAISY*
◊ *FERN GULLY*
◊ *FLOWERS FOR ALGERNON*
◊ *PLEASE DON'T EAT THE DAISIES*
◊ *ROSEMARY'S BABY*
◊ *SNOW FLOWER AND THE SECRET FAN*
◊ *STEEL MAGNOLIAS*
◊ *THE BEST EXOTIC MARIGOLD HOTEL*
◊ *THE BLACK DAHLIA*
◊ *THE BLACK ORCHID*
◊ *THE DAY OF THE TRIFFIDS*
◊ *THE LAVENDER HILL MOB*
◊ *THE PLACE BEYOND THE PINES*
◊ *THE SEA OF TREES*
◊ *THE TREE OF LIFE*
◊ *THE WAR OF THE ROSES*
◊ *THE WIND IN THE WILLOWS*
◊ *THROUGH THE OLIVE TREES*
◊ *UNDER THE TREE*

77 National Forests of the USA

T R O I N I T A L L A G A R I
N D A E H T A L F E D I X I E
C H U G A C H J M A Y E E A R
Y E C R E P Z E N E L C N E E
R I O G R A N D E Y S I T T V
R J E S E T H S U M C T G O I
A O K O O T E N A I E H D N R
R C I N O T Q N M M G A D G E
R I T R T U T S A E N E A A T
E O R E E I A L I O B L G S I
I A Y S L P L C R U O O F S H
S A A A F I U O H B S O I H W
P E S W W A C S I I X L O S H
S A N J U A N C W G T H A S E
L O S P A D R E S U R A Y W H

◊ BOISE
◊ CHUGACH
◊ CIBOLA
◊ CORONADO
◊ DIXIE
◊ EL YUNQUE
◊ FLATHEAD
◊ GALLATIN
◊ GILA
◊ KOOTENAI
◊ LOS PADRES
◊ MANTI-LA SAL
◊ NEZ PERCE
◊ OUACHITA
◊ PAYETTE
◊ RIO GRANDE
◊ SAN JUAN
◊ SIERRA
◊ SIUSLAW
◊ SUPERIOR
◊ TONGASS
◊ TONTO
◊ WHITE RIVER
◊ WILLAMETTE

78

Alfred Lord Tennyson – *The Flower* (1842)

Once in a golden hour
I cast to earth a seed.
Up there came a flower,
The people said, a weed.
To and fro they went
Thro' my garden-bower,
And muttering discontent
Cursed me and my flower.
Then it grew so tall
It wore a crown of light,
But thieves from o'er the wall
Stole the seed by night.
Sow'd it far and wide
By every town and tower,
Till all the people cried
`Splendid is the flower.'
Read my little fable:
He that runs may read.
Most can raise the flowers
now,
For all have got the seed.
And some are pretty enough,
And some are poor indeed;
And now again the people
Call it but a weed.

And binding with briars, my
joys & desires.

79 Orchids (Common Names)

G	D	F	F	J	T	K	C	U	D	E	G	R	A	L
O	E	E	T	R	M	A	U	A	N	A	K	W	U	L
R	A	P	P	O	V	O	C	A	G	S	B	P	L	C
F	S	E	N	I	S	T	Y	E	U	L	Y	U	N	U
U	T	K	W	P	R	A	F	M	L	R	B	A	P	C
U	E	N	Y	A	L	T	B	I	A	G	K	I	H	U
Y	R	L	E	A	X	U	S	M	R	E	N	M	W	M
D	A	E	M	S	R	L	I	O	D	E	D	U	S	B
C	E	I	P	N	W	D	I	M	A	O	S	V	J	E
C	H	R	T	P	A	R	A	P	H	S	Y	T	S	R
T	B	T	L	L	I	N	P	S	B	E	H	Y	A	A
N	I	B	W	A	X	L	E	P	N	N	A	W	S	R
P	N	G	J	E	E	F	S	B	D	U	C	L	G	U
U	F	N	E	C	X	E	V	O	R	G	N	A	M	A
F	R	A	G	R	A	N	T	M	U	L	E	E	A	R

◊ BULL ORCHID
◊ BURNT-TIP ORCHID
◊ CALYPSO
◊ CUCUMBER ORCHID
◊ EASTER ORCHID
◊ FIRE-STAR ORCHID
◊ FRAGRANT ORCHID
◊ FROG ORCHID
◊ HIMALAYAN CROCUS
◊ JUNGLE CAT ORCHID
◊ LARGE DUCK ORCHID
◊ MANGROVE ORCHID
◊ MONKEY ORCHID
◊ MULE EAR ORCHID
◊ MUSK ORCHID
◊ NAKED MAN ORCHID
◊ NUN'S ORCHID
◊ PINEAPPLE ORCHID
◊ PYRAMIDAL ORCHID
◊ SLIPPER ORCHID
◊ STRIPED CORALROOT
◊ SWAN ORCHID
◊ TIGER ORCHID
◊ WAX LIP ORCHID

80 Genera in the Family: Rosaceae – Part Three (Rose Family)

F	I	N	E	A	I	N	I	L	E	U	Q	U	A	V
A	E	A	R	I	P	S	O	R	E	X	U	S	S	O
M	L	J	I	R	H	O	L	O	D	I	S	C	U	S
A	E	L	U	R	F	R	A	G	A	R	I	A	P	M
V	F	N	E	N	A	I	N	O	D	Y	C	A	R	D
S	U	A	C	Y	O	B	E	N	C	O	M	I	A	R
S	E	L	I	H	E	P	R	P	C	A	A	S	C	Y
I	A	N	G	L	A	L	A	O	A	N	I	R	O	M
E	E	Y	A	S	L	D	D	E	S	P	P	E	C	O
V	C	S	U	H	E	I	D	N	H	A	E	V	R	C
E	B	U	G	L	P	I	E	O	I	U	S	A	E	A
R	N	B	L	X	T	A	R	N	V	L	N	I	C	L
S	R	U	H	A	A	A	O	E	E	L	I	S	E	L
I	S	R	B	T	O	R	M	I	N	A	R	I	A	I
A	I	A	I	N	A	W	O	C	U	P	P	G	N	S

- ◊ *APHANES*
- ◊ *ARONIA*
- ◊ *BATIDEA*
- ◊ *BENCOMIA*
- ◊ *CERCOCARPUS*
- ◊ *COWANIA*
- ◊ *CYDONIA*
- ◊ *DASIPHORA*
- ◊ *DRYMOCALLIS*
- ◊ *FRAGARIA*
- ◊ *HOLODISCUS*
- ◊ *LINDLEYELLA*
- ◊ *NEILLIA*
- ◊ *PADELLUS*
- ◊ *PRINSEPIA*
- ◊ *PRUNUS*
- ◊ *RUBUS*
- ◊ *SIEVERSIA*
- ◊ *SORBARIA*
- ◊ *TORMINARIA*
- ◊ *VAUQUELINIA*
- ◊ *XEROSPIRAEA*

81

Plants with Beautiful and Strange Flowers (Common Names)

A	S	R	T	E	R	I	A	T	A	N	S	I	A	Y
G	A	L	A	S	L	I	V	E	D	E	D	O	F	D
W	E	D	F	T	G	N	I	D	E	E	L	B	E	A
M	R	L	O	B	S	T	E	R	C	L	A	W	S	S
P	O	T	D	E	L	D	D	A	W	S	F	M	N	A
A	T	N	W	F	D	F	F	T	W	G	W	I	M	D
S	N	A	K	E	W	T	N	H	P	E	W	J	Y	N
S	B	U	A	E	A	R	I	L	V	R	M	E	W	A
I	D	Y	N	B	Y	T	E	I	A	M	O	O	L	P
O	R	E	G	G	E	R	H	D	U	K	R	T	T	U
N	E	H	E	N	F	E	E	E	I	V	C	D	E	H
A	T	C	L	V	E	N	E	G	H	P	X	A	L	A
K	L	L	A	B	N	O	N	N	A	C	S	G	J	S
E	E	B	E	L	B	M	U	B	U	L	I	T	I	A
D	I	T	O	R	R	A	P	S	T	U	R	T	S	E

◊ ANGEL ORCHID
◊ BAT FACED CUPHEA
◊ BEEHIVE GINGER
◊ BLEEDING HEART
◊ BUMBLEBEE ORCHID
◊ CANNONBALL TREE
◊ DARWIN'S SLIPPER
◊ DEVIL'S HAND TREE
◊ JACKAL FOOD
◊ LOBSTER-CLAWS
◊ MONKEY FACE ORCHID
◊ MOTH ORCHID
◊ NAKED MAN ORCHID
◊ PANDA FACE GINGER
◊ PARROT FLOWER
◊ PASSION FLOWER
◊ PROTEA PINWHEEL
◊ REGAL BIRDFLOWER
◊ SNAKE GOURD
◊ SPIDER CHRYSANTHEMUM
◊ STAR FLOWER
◊ STURT'S DESERT PEA
◊ SWADDLED BABIES
◊ WHITE BATFLOWER

82

Moisture-Loving Plants (Common Names)

◊ AMERICAN PUSSY WILLOW
◊ BANEBERRY
◊ BLEEDING HEART
◊ BOGBEAN
◊ BRAZILIAN GIANT-RHUBARB
◊ BROOKLIME
◊ CALLA LILY
◊ CANDELABRA PRIMROSE
◊ CARDINAL FLOWER
◊ CATTAIL
◊ CINNAMON FERN
◊ CORKSCREW RUSH
◊ DWARF BULRUSH
◊ FALSE GOAT'S BEARD
◊ LEOPARD PLANT
◊ LESSER SPEARWORT
◊ PAPER REED
◊ PICKEREL WEED
◊ PURPLE LOOSESTRIFE
◊ SUMMERSWEET
◊ SWAMP SUNFLOWER
◊ TRUE FORGET-ME-NOT
◊ WATER HAWTHORN
◊ YELLOW FLAG

83 Parasitic Plants (Common Names)

```
N R E H T R O N G H O S T E G
P R A L A U T R N D U R S A G
N E U C P V T I A M W R N S I
M A I H I R Y A M N J F O D U
S P I X T D U E J L G A W B R
N A M D I T R P Y W S E U A D
V O N E N B E E C H V R J S N
A P M D H I L P R A R D T N U
J H O M F L D L N O O E U A O
D A M N O O O C W O E R S M R
K L E W P C O E M W S S A H G
E M E L G U E D S U P W M C J
Y D L I V D U D E V I L S T U
P I N E F O O T B A Y O R U M
N U R R A M P I N E W O O D S
```

◊ ACID DROPS
◊ BEECH DROPS
◊ BURROWEED STRANGLER
◊ COMMON COMANDRA
◊ DEVIL'S TWINE
◊ DUTCHMAN'S PIPE
◊ FIELD DODDER
◊ GHOST PLANT
◊ GROUND PINEAPPLE
◊ HEMP BROOMRAPE
◊ INDIAN PAINTBRUSH
◊ MOODJAR
◊ NORTHERN VAMPIRE CUP
◊ OAK MISTLETOE
◊ ORANGE MISTLETOE
◊ PINEFOOT
◊ PINEWOODS LOUSEWORT
◊ PURPLE WITCHWEED
◊ SANDFOOD
◊ SNOW PLANT
◊ SUMMER CORALROOT
◊ SWEET PINESAP
◊ VANCOUVER GROUNDCONE
◊ YELLOW RATTLE

84 Trees of Africa (Common Names)

A L L E R B M U O L A F F U B
D L E F M M L A P A L A L R F
E A I N Y O P J O N A R B E Z
K S G J A R P E S L A F V G D
I A N A N C N A O V E E N O D
P U S C H G I O N G R A O P O
S S F K M A S R B E D W H U O
A A S A S M E A F A D Y E R W
L G Y L A G N A P A G N A P E
U E N B B D J D E E C H E L Z
R D U E I B N L I U Z H I E E
A Y R R E B P A O S E N U D E
M A O R I Y D E T U L F U I N
B B Y Y X M T V I A E V R U S
A J I B A B O A B S L E R A M

- ◊ AFRICAN CORKWOOD TREE
- ◊ ANDIROBA
- ◊ BAOBAB
- ◊ BUFFALO THORN
- ◊ DUNE SOAP-BERRY
- ◊ FALSE ASSEGAI
- ◊ FEVER TREE
- ◊ FLUTED MILKWOOD
- ◊ GABON EBONY
- ◊ JACKALBERRY
- ◊ LALA PALM
- ◊ LEADWOOD
- ◊ MARULA TREE
- ◊ MOPANE TREE
- ◊ MSASA
- ◊ MU'UNZE
- ◊ NATAL MAHOGANY
- ◊ PANGA PANGA
- ◊ PURPLE CORALTREE
- ◊ SAUSAGE TREE
- ◊ SNEEZEWOOD TREE
- ◊ SPIKED CABBAGE TREE
- ◊ UMBRELLA THORN ACACIA
- ◊ ZEBRANO

85 Female Botanists – Part One

N	O	S	K	C	I	R	E	C	X	L	A	N	D	A
S	O	V	B	H	B	M	Y	R	W	A	R	N	E	S
A	C	O	U	M	T	R	L	U	V	A	M	L	P	E
B	R	Y	E	N	P	I	A	O	G	A	S	O	A	M
A	A	F	C	R	A	N	W	V	H	M	B	U	L	M
D	N	W	A	A	E	M	A	K	O	Y	Y	N	M	A
A	W	B	O	L	R	Z	E	F	C	O	N	S	E	T
H	E	Y	L	O	A	T	Y	N	U	E	T	B	R	F
L	L	A	V	H	L	H	U	M	O	G	B	E	R	I
G	L	B	A	J	J	W	A	D	E	T	A	R	E	N
R	P	V	V	A	H	N	A	G	J	R	S	R	K	N
E	I	H	M	E	S	M	L	R	B	R	F	Y	O	E
N	J	M	I	I	S	Y	E	E	D	I	O	S	O	G
I	A	J	D	I	E	T	R	I	C	H	R	O	H	A
L	N	O	S	T	R	E	B	L	A	L	D	N	G	N

◊ MARY ALBERTSON

◊ RUTH F. ALLEN

◊ JANAKI AMMAL

◊ AGNES ARBER

◊ KATHLEEN BASFORD

◊ ANGIE BECKWITH

◊ HELIA BRAVO

◊ LUCY CRANWELL

◊ GERTRUD DAHLGREN

◊ AMALIE DIETRICH

◊ RICA ERICKSON

◊ JEAN FINNEGAN

◊ HENRIETTA HOOKER

◊ ELIZABETH LOMAX

◊ ALICE LOUNSBERRY

◊ ELSA NYHOLM

◊ EVE PALMER

◊ GABRIELE RABEL

◊ BERTHA STONEMAN

◊ JANTINA TAMMES

◊ CLARISSA TRACY

◊ FLORENCE WOOLWARD

◊ ELIZA ANN YOUMANS

◊ AVISHAG ZAHAVI

86 Shrubs – Part Two (Common Names)

E	Y	D	C	A	A	P	R	C	A	L	U	G	Y	Y
N	N	L	O	C	I	L	H	E	A	T	H	E	R	R
E	B	I	L	G	B	H	O	R	P	C	G	R	W	C
R	L	U	M	O	W	E	T	R	A	I	W	G	G	T
E	S	K	R	S	H	O	N	Y	E	L	N	U	Y	R
H	K	R	Y	H	A	I	O	T	S	C	D	U	X	E
P	I	A	F	I	S	J	H	D	E	R	A	E	J	E
H	M	B	S	U	H	T	N	A	M	S	O	S	M	P
O	M	E	I	F	P	A	E	J	T	O	Y	F	O	E
T	I	C	A	S	L	U	N	E	O	A	O	U	S	O
I	A	A	R	U	C	C	I	C	W	J	R	R	F	N
N	I	L	P	A	A	U	J	G	T	S	O	A	B	Y
I	E	I	W	L	N	B	S	M	N	G	W	B	W	E
A	N	A	I	P	E	A	R	L	B	U	S	H	A	H
O	G	L	O	R	Y	B	O	W	E	R	S	M	R	J

◊ ACEROLA
◊ AUCUBA
◊ BROOM
◊ DOGWOOD
◊ FORSYTHIA
◊ GLORYBOWER
◊ GORSE
◊ HEATHER
◊ HIBISCUS
◊ HOLLY
◊ JASMINE
◊ JOJOBA
◊ JUNIPER
◊ LACEBARK
◊ LILAC
◊ LUPIN
◊ MEDLAR
◊ OSMANTHUS
◊ PEARL BUSH
◊ PHOTINIA
◊ SKIMMIA
◊ SWEETSHRUB
◊ TREE-PEONY
◊ WARATAH

87

Fern Genera and Species (Common Names)

L R D L E I H S T F O S V A B
I L I L O L Y V A C R A B E D
I B D A I C J N R O H G A T S
H R N N H I H K F C H A I N R
E A C L O S T R I C H O E H A
P C W A K M U A I M O T O C B
A K K Y A T M N U S B A J E B
C E L O N S Y O E T T E L E I
K N I R G P S H C V U M R B T
C R D N A N X T N C F M A L S
O E E O R G I O R H M R N S Y
R H E T O B T G A A O M D B A
N T R T O S P R N U H U R A S
I O F U O I D G G A W V S N E
L M E B T E T H I T H R G E P

- ◊ AUTUMN FERN
- ◊ BEECH FERN
- ◊ BOSTON FERN
- ◊ BRACKEN
- ◊ BUTTON FERN
- ◊ CHAIN FERN
- ◊ CHRISTMAS FERN
- ◊ COMMON POLYPODY
- ◊ DEER FERN
- ◊ HANGING FORK FERN
- ◊ HART'S TONGUE FERN
- ◊ HOUSE HOLLY-FERN
- ◊ KANGAROO FERN
- ◊ KIMBERLY QUEEN FERN
- ◊ MOTHER SPLEENWORT
- ◊ OAK FERN
- ◊ OSTRICH FERN
- ◊ RABBIT'S FOOT FERN
- ◊ ROCKCAP FERN
- ◊ ROUGH MAIDENHAIR FERN
- ◊ ROYAL FERN
- ◊ SOFT SHIELD FERN
- ◊ STAGHORN FERN
- ◊ VENUS HAIR FERN

88 Wonderful Woods, Fantastic Forests, and Glorious Groves

M A N A I N O D E L A C E R I
S E N A G U J U F B L A C K D
O S A G A N O A L J A I H T O
A B U I D S C G A A T Y A A O
U O M G Q U H M I N B I S K W
O C M O J L I E A A R A A N D
P O R I I H A L R A H O N A E
I N T C S M T C C W K Z T I R
A G C U Y A Y U A R O N U V K
W O K E A M A Z O N A O T I U
E A A J M R H C L M D F D D J
Y H I M A L A Y A N B O B L N
V R U G R E A T B E A R N A E
R O Z B E L L A V I S T A V T
E E R T N I A D D E K O O R C

- ◊ AMAZON RAINFOREST
- ◊ ARAUCARIA MOIST FORESTS
- ◊ ATLANTIC FOREST
- ◊ BELLAVISTA CLOUD FOREST
- ◊ BLACK FOREST
- ◊ CALEDONIAN FOREST
- ◊ CONGO BASIN FOREST
- ◊ CORK OAK FORESTS
- ◊ CROOKED FOREST
- ◊ DAINTREE RAINFOREST
- ◊ GREAT BEAR RAINFOREST
- ◊ HIMALAYAN SUBTROPICAL PINE FORESTS
- ◊ JIUZHAIGOU VALLEY
- ◊ KINABALU PARK
- ◊ LACANDON JUNGLE
- ◊ MIOMBO WOODLANDS
- ◊ REDWOOD NATIONAL PARKS
- ◊ SAGANO BAMBOO FOREST
- ◊ SHERWOOD FOREST
- ◊ TAMAN NEGARA
- ◊ TIJUCA FOREST
- ◊ VALDIVIAN TEMPERATE FORESTS
- ◊ WAIPOUA FOREST
- ◊ YAKUSHIMA FOREST

89 Moss Genera – Part Two

- ◊ *AMBLYTROPIS*
- ◊ *ARCHIDIUM*
- ◊ *BARBULA*
- ◊ *BRYMELA*
- ◊ *CALOMNION*
- ◊ *COSTESIA*
- ◊ *DIPHYSCIUM*
- ◊ *FONTINALIS*
- ◊ *GAROVAGLIA*
- ◊ *HOOKERIA*
- ◊ *LEUCOLEPIS*
- ◊ *LIMBELLA*
- ◊ *OCHYRAEA*
- ◊ *PHYSCOMITRELLA*
- ◊ *PHYSCOMITRIUM*
- ◊ *PLAGIOMNIUM*
- ◊ *PTILIUM*
- ◊ *SELIGERIA*
- ◊ *SPHAGNUM*
- ◊ *TAYLORIA*

Plant- and Flower-Related Literary Character Names

U	A	L	A	C	Y	Y	Y	P	P	O	P	H	F	I
N	E	M	E	T	C	S	L	W	A	L	E	Y	T	A
D	L	O	E	R	X	R	I	P	N	E	W	A	U	I
Y	A	O	S	E	U	V	L	A	M	O	L	C	G	N
S	V	L	O	E	S	A	W	N	D	Y	J	I	M	U
F	E	B	R	B	E	O	L	S	Y	H	R	N	P	T
G	N	T	M	E	R	E	A	Y	T	E	F	T	A	E
M	D	S	I	A	A	T	H	P	N	A	L	H	L	P
V	E	B	R	R	N	T	H	R	Y	T	E	D	N	E
I	R	A	P	D	M	O	O	B	G	H	U	U	V	B
O	W	S	A	I	L	H	A	D	N	E	R	B	P	L
L	O	I	U	L	T	Y	N	O	I	R	B	A	A	D
E	N	L	Y	W	A	R	N	E	S	A	R	S	Z	R
T	E	Y	A	P	I	E	R	F	D	F	L	O	R	A
E	S	H	N	A	R	C	I	S	S	A	Y	R	E	R

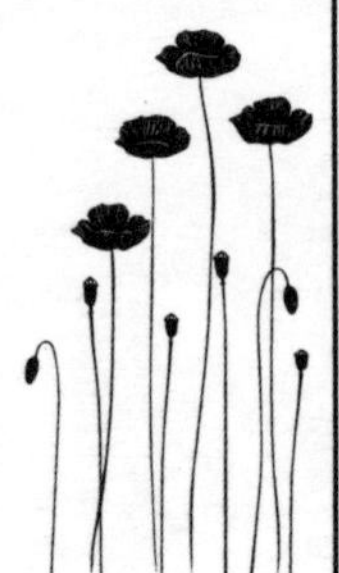

- ◊ AUNT DAHLIA
- ◊ BASIL HALLWARD
- ◊ BRIONY TALLIS
- ◊ DAISY BUCHANAN
- ◊ FLEUR DELACOUR
- ◊ FLORA FINCHING
- ◊ GALE HAWTHORNE
- ◊ HEATHER HART
- ◊ HOLLY GOLIGHTLY
- ◊ HYACINTH ROBINSON
- ◊ LAUREL STEVENSON
- ◊ LAVENDER LEWIS
- ◊ LEOPOLD BLOOM
- ◊ LILY OWENS
- ◊ MOANING MYRTLE
- ◊ NARCISSA MALFOY
- ◊ PANSY PARKINSON
- ◊ PETUNIA DURSELY
- ◊ POPPY POMFREY
- ◊ PRIMROSE EVERDEEN
- ◊ ROSA BUD
- ◊ ROWAN MAYFAIR
- ◊ TREEBEARD
- ◊ VIOLET BEAUREGARDE

91 Botany Books

B C E G N A H C U B A F H E T
I O A A I F L O W E R S A S R
Z N T D A R W I N S W E I R D
A M E A R T I S T S H T S R A
R P B R N O F A T H E R S L U
R F L G J Y L E N R H M E M G
E S L A C I T C A R P A M U H
N J R J N J C B B J H L L C T
F A Y E V T A T L A S Y R I E
I E T S T C S Z A A P I A N R
W E S U E N P L S A T V V A F
A A C H R C U U S E Y I E T L
L R T Y X E P H F T E F N O O
G N I R E H T A G H E R S B R
L A N D E S R E D D A L T S A

- ◊ *A GARDENER'S LATIN*
- ◊ *BIZARRE BOTANY*
- ◊ *BOTANICUM*
- ◊ *BOTANY FOR ARTISTS*
- ◊ *DARWIN'S MOST WONDERFUL PLANTS*
- ◊ *FATHERS OF BOTANY*
- ◊ *FLORA: INSIDE THE SECRET WORLD OF PLANTS*
- ◊ *GATHERING MOSS*
- ◊ *LADDERS TO HEAVEN*
- ◊ *PRACTICAL BOTANY FOR GARDENERS*
- ◊ *RAVEN BIOLOGY OF PLANTS*
- ◊ *SEEDS OF CHANGE*
- ◊ *THE BIG, BAD BOOK OF BOTANY*
- ◊ *THE BOTANICAL ATLAS*
- ◊ *THE BOTANIST'S DAUGHTER*
- ◊ *THE BRIEF LIFE OF FLOWERS*
- ◊ *THE CABARET OF PLANTS*
- ◊ *THE HIDDEN LIFE OF TREES*
- ◊ *THE IMMORTAL YEW*
- ◊ *THE PLANT HUNTERS*
- ◊ *THE PLANT MESSIAH*
- ◊ *THE LITTLE BOOK OF MEDICINAL PLANTS*
- ◊ *THE SECRET NETWORK OF NATURE*
- ◊ *WEIRD PLANTS*

92 Asteroids and Minor Planets Named for Plants

H	E	U	R	N	G	R	U	M	U	I	L	I	L	U
E	S	I	L	L	Y	R	A	M	A	I	S	M	U	A
D	A	M	C	A	E	L	A	Z	A	C	Y	A	P	I
E	C	S	S	E	S	Q	U	I	A	P	R	L	R	T
R	H	H	U	I	D	S	I	M	B	Y	I	V	I	Y
A	E	U	H	C	O	R	P	I	D	E	N	A	M	S
U	M	C	T	P	O	A	U	T	U	B	G	U	U	R
Y	R	N	N	J	N	R	I	S	G	A	A	S	L	O
O	T	M	A	U	C	Q	C	J	P	Y	S	S	A	F
G	C	C	L	E	M	A	T	I	S	E	A	T	F	R
S	I	A	A	P	H	V	L	R	R	L	A	S	E	A
A	P	N	G	Y	I	U	E	P	V	A	E	S	A	R
L	G	G	K	O	T	C	U	I	M	Y	R	T	U	S
I	E	H	L	G	A	C	A	R	A	I	N	D	A	H
X	C	A	A	S	O	Y	E	A	H	T	N	E	M	Z

- ◊ 8833 ACER (MAPLE)
- ◊ 1085 AMARYLLIS (AMARYLLIS)
- ◊ 1218 ASTER (ASTER)
- ◊ 1056 AZALEA (AZALEA)
- ◊ 1077 CAMPANULA (BELLFLOWER)
- ◊ 8657 CEDRUS (CEDAR)
- ◊ 1101 CLEMATIS (CLEMATIS)
- ◊ 1220 CROCUS (CROCUS)
- ◊ 8656 CUPRESSUS (CYPRESS)
- ◊ 1054 FORSYTIA (FORSYTHIA)
- ◊ 1250 GALANTHUS (SNOWDROP)
- ◊ 85197 GINKGO (GINGKO TREE)
- ◊ 1251 HEDERA (IVY)
- ◊ 1092 LILIUM (LILY)
- ◊ 1072 MALVA (MALLOW)
- ◊ 1078 MENTHA (MINT)
- ◊ 9203 MYRTUS (MYRTLE)
- ◊ 1080 ORCHIS (ORCHID)
- ◊ 970 PRIMULA (PRIMROSE)
- ◊ 8648 SALIX (WILLOW)
- ◊ 1083 SALVIA (SAGE)
- ◊ 1104 SYRINGA (LILAC)
- ◊ 1095 TULIPA (TULIP)
- ◊ 1076 VIOLA (VIOLET)

93 Unusual Plant Nicknames – Part Two

J	T	R	O	W	E	Z	E	E	N	S	B	A	O	E
B	U	T	C	H	E	R	S	U	I	C	A	O	R	L
S	L	E	R	R	I	U	Q	S	U	Y	R	L	A	E
S	W	M	O	N	K	E	Y	P	N	A	M	L	R	P
E	K	I	P	S	E	R	I	F	G	O	I	A	L	H
G	Y	Y	N	S	H	D	B	N	S	U	B	B	M	A
R	A	M	W	E	S	A	A	J	U	E	F	E	T	N
A	A	O	N	R	S	K	M	A	U	Q	M	S	O	T
T	R	B	U	G	L	E	W	E	E	D	Y	A	H	F
C	P	O	N	Y	T	A	I	L	P	N	G	B	D	O
S	S	K	C	A	L	B	B	J	O	L	G	F	E	O
C	O	R	N	C	O	C	K	L	E	S	A	S	R	T
Y	C	R	A	S	G	N	I	Y	L	F	H	N	S	A
F	G	T	D	E	S	P	R	O	C	Y	S	W	T	L
R	E	T	T	U	B	N	A	K	E	D	M	A	N	E

◊ BASEBALL PLANT
◊ BEAR'S BREECHES
◊ BLACK BAT FLOWER
◊ BUGLEWEED
◊ BUTCHER'S BROOM
◊ BUTTER AND EGGS
◊ CORNCOCKLES
◊ CORPSE FLOWER
◊ CROW'S TOES
◊ CUPID'S DART
◊ DAME'S ROCKET
◊ ELEPHANT-FOOT YAM
◊ FIRESPIKE
◊ FLYING DUCK ORCHID
◊ KANGAROO PAWS
◊ MONKEY PUZZLE TREE
◊ NAKED MAN ORCHID
◊ PONYTAIL PALM
◊ RED-HOT POKERS
◊ SHAGGY SOLDIER
◊ SHAMEPLANT
◊ SNEEZEWORT
◊ SQUIRREL CORN
◊ SWINE'S SNOUT

Bands and Musicians with Plant-Related Names

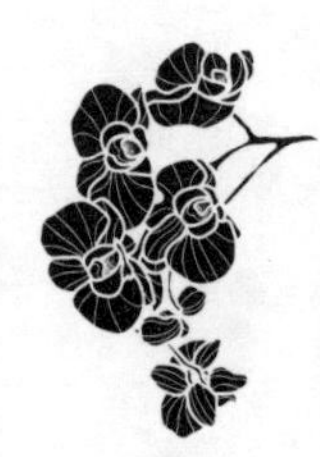

W A L L F L O W E R S I C R U
O O N P S B T N A L P Y C A Y
L T Y N U U O W L Y P E D E W
L V R S O C T E U R G E H S S
I I H E C D Z C E Y S F N M E
W T E A E A A S A O L G O L S
L K V N H S S L R C U N I A O
T A O L I V E T L N N B L P R
A O R E G P R O S E L E E U E
D E A L T E U N R O B T D M N
A Y M S S A R C S C P R N P O
H W C E N O E S R I H X A K T
L P D D S R O H E O V I D I S
I U D E A M A C W I P W D N T
A W S E S U N F L O W E R S O

- ◊ BELLADONNA
- ◊ BLOSSOMS
- ◊ CACTUS
- ◊ CYPRESS HILL
- ◊ DANDELION
- ◊ GUNS N' ROSES
- ◊ HAZEL
- ◊ IVY
- ◊ KATE BUSH
- ◊ OLIVE
- ◊ PALMS
- ◊ PORCUPINE TREE
- ◊ ROBERT PLANT
- ◊ SCREAMING TREES
- ◊ SMASHING PUMPKINS
- ◊ SUNFLOWER BEAN
- ◊ THE BLACK DAHLIA MURDER
- ◊ THE DESERT ROSE BAND
- ◊ THE ORCHIDS
- ◊ THE STONE ROSES
- ◊ THE WALLFLOWERS
- ◊ WHEAT
- ◊ WHITE WILLOW
- ◊ WYE OAK

95

Plant-Related Deities, Gods, and Spirits

```
S G L A N T H O U S A I A R L
U A A R A N Y A N I D R D E F
L X B Y D O F I I T O A E Y G
L A X O R P N U L L P N Y O R
E O O E N S O E F H E E E R G
C N C G A B S M N L S S L X D
U I H R X H A E O I U U X A A
S Y I A Y S V D R N I N M A N
T N Q N E R U O E K A A S K I
C A U D D I L N K X M V E M E
C S E B V H N I U A T L L U D
E O T O C R L S H A L I V Y E
R W Z I R E E C P U F S A R M
E I A S I U A I D B E R N E X
S E L M H P O C Y U A C S I I
```

- ◊ ABNOBA (GAULISH)
- ◊ ANTHOUSAI (GREEK)
- ◊ ARANYANI (HINDU)
- ◊ CERES (ROMAN)
- ◊ CHLORIS (GREEK)
- ◊ DAPHNE (GREEK)
- ◊ DRYADS (GREEK)
- ◊ FAUNUS (ROMAN)
- ◊ FLORA (ROMAN)
- ◊ FUFLUNS (ROMAN)
- ◊ GRAND BOIS (HAITIAN VOODOO)
- ◊ LESHY (SLAVIC)
- ◊ MEDEINA (LITHUANIAN)
- ◊ MIELIKKI (FINNISH)
- ◊ NINSAR (SUMERIAN)
- ◊ OSANYIN (YORUBA)
- ◊ PACHAMAMA (INCA)
- ◊ POMONA (ROMAN)
- ◊ SELVANS (ETRUSCAN)
- ◊ SILVANUS (ROMAN)
- ◊ SUCELLUS (CELTIC)
- ◊ TAPIO (FINNISH)
- ◊ XOCHIQUETZAL (AZTEC)
- ◊ YUM KAAX (MAYAN)

96

Elizabeth Barrett Browing – *Beloved, thou hast brought me many flowers* (1850)

E	G	L	A	N	T	I	N	E	D	R	A	G	S	N
L	L	A	H	S	S	H	O	W	E	R	S	E	R	W
E	N	I	P	R	U	R	E	W	U	S	M	T	E	D
E	K	A	T	U	S	N	O	U	I	A	X	R	W	E
T	I	A	W	O	L	D	F	O	N	N	G	W	O	V
I	H	Y	U	L	L	L	V	O	T	G	T	E	B	O
R	V	L	S	O	I	E	E	G	L	S	D	E	B	L
E	P	Y	C	C	R	O	V	T	D	D	E	D	R	E
M	E	M	T	G	C	L	O	S	E	N	E	S	E	B
M	E	L	R	O	S	M	S	Y	A	D	U	D	W	S
U	K	O	U	A	I	T	S	T	H	G	U	O	H	T
S	W	S	E	N	W	F	L	F	L	O	W	E	R	S
N	E	E	E	U	W	E	R	D	H	T	I	W	W	G
D	D	E	K	C	U	L	P	W	E	E	D	I	N	G
S	T	R	A	E	H	I	N	S	T	R	U	C	T	A

Beloved, thou hast brought me many flowers
Plucked in the garden, all the summer through
And winter, and it seemed as if they grew
In this close room, nor missed the sun and showers,
So, in the like name of that love of ours,
Take back these thoughts which here unfolded too,
And which on warm and cold days I withdrew
From my heart's ground. Indeed, those beds and bowers
Be overgrown with bitter weeds and rue,
And wait thy weeding; yet here's eglantine,
Here's ivy!— take them, as I used to do
Thy flowers, and keep them where they shall not pine.
Instruct thine eyes to keep their colours true,
And tell thy soul, their roots are left in mine.

Great Gardens

U	B	H	C	S	O	B	N	E	T	S	R	I	K	V
N	I	S	K	E	W	G	A	R	D	E	N	S	E	A
N	S	N	T	R	U	O	C	S	R	E	W	O	P	C
K	E	A	N	S	E	A	L	U	C	H	S	E	N	I
B	T	U	T	A	U	V	D	A	A	T	G	E	V	F
U	U	N	K	R	E	C	S	N	R	P	A	S	R	I
T	D	A	I	O	F	D	D	N	U	H	S	F	I	T
C	U	L	N	D	R	W	M	O	N	E	T	S	T	R
H	E	O	C	E	R	N	R	N	D	I	V	E	I	M
A	M	L	T	A	I	A	E	G	E	I	O	H	E	I
R	U	S	B	U	O	Y	J	K	L	Y	C	T	K	D
T	A	L	I	M	A	H	U	L	I	P	R	A	U	R
M	C	A	R	I	U	U	A	V	P	A	A	R	P	A
K	E	U	K	E	N	H	O	F	Y	H	P	C	I	J
L	E	V	A	N	U	A	S	A	Z	O	P	S	A	L

- ◊ ARUNDEL CASTLE GARDENS (UK)
- ◊ BUTCHART GARDENS (CANADA)
- ◊ CRATHES CASTLE (UK)
- ◊ DESERT BOTANICAL GARDEN (USA)
- ◊ HUMBLE ADMINISTRATOR'S GARDEN (CHINA)
- ◊ JARDIM BOTANICO (BRAZIL)
- ◊ JARDIN MAJORELLE (MOROCCO)
- ◊ KENROKU-EN (JAPAN)
- ◊ KEUKENHOF (NETHERLANDS)
- ◊ KEW GARDENS (UK)
- ◊ KIRSTENBOSCH (SOUTH AFRICA)
- ◊ LAS POZAS (MEXICO)
- ◊ LIMAHULI GARDEN (USA)
- ◊ MASTER OF NETS GARDEN (CHINA)
- ◊ MONET'S GARDENS (FRANCE)
- ◊ PARCO SAN GRATO (SWITZERLAND)
- ◊ POWERSCOURT GARDENS (IRELAND)
- ◊ PUKEITI GARDENS (NEW ZEALAND)
- ◊ SUAN NONG NOOCH GARDEN (THAILAND)
- ◊ VILLA D'ESTE (ITALY)

Plants That Appear in Myths and Legends

C	A	V	A	B	A	Y	L	A	U	R	E	L	E	P
E	I	N	O	I	T	A	N	R	A	C	S	C	A	L
N	H	E	Y	R	L	P	E	S	H	U	W	I	S	S
O	O	T	O	P	R	W	D	H	S	V	A	R	E	G
M	R	S	U	G	O	O	N	S	L	R	E	N	S	O
E	E	F	G	L	R	I	I	I	N	W	A	A	A	T
N	H	H	F	E	I	C	L	I	O	B	W	P	H	U
A	O	N	G	N	R	P	C	L	S	V	R	E	U	K
U	U	A	I	A	H	A	F	F	S	U	T	O	L	O
S	N	S	N	A	U	N	L	N	U	Y	E	N	W	L
O	D	P	Z	S	R	O	H	C	R	I	B	Y	R	A
O	N	E	A	O	W	I	L	D	C	H	E	R	R	Y
E	L	N	C	H	E	N	A	W	O	R	H	I	A	F
H	E	N	B	A	N	E	H	T	N	I	C	A	Y	H
W	S	R	G	E	E	R	T	N	A	Y	N	A	B	I

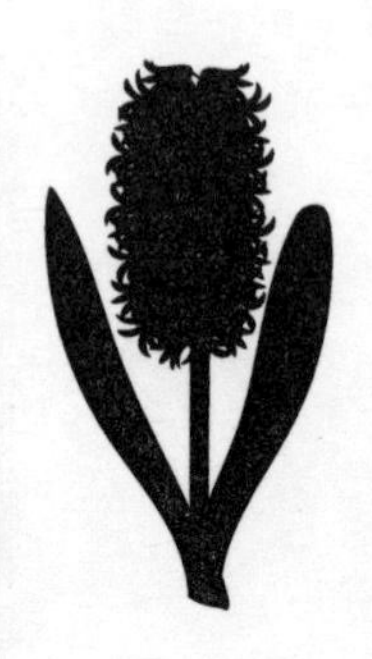

◊ ANEMONE
◊ ARNICA
◊ ASPEN
◊ BANYAN TREE
◊ BAY LAUREL
◊ BIRCH
◊ CARNATION
◊ CORNFLOWERS
◊ GOTU KOLA
◊ HAZEL
◊ HENBANE
◊ HOREHOUND
◊ HYACINTH
◊ LINDEN
◊ LOTUS
◊ NARCISSUS
◊ OREGANO
◊ PEONY
◊ ROSE
◊ ROWAN
◊ SUNFLOWER
◊ TULIP
◊ WILD CHERRY
◊ WOLFSBANE

99 Plants in *The Complete Herbal* by Nicholas Culpeper – Part Two

S D E E W P A N K Y A T G E P

P I F A B P O B P E N M D M N

V X E O I I R E E I S N E V A

A S M C O A S R G Y O H F H N

I T O H B H T T N A V O X N C

S O T U E M E O O F S I T E V

Y R H H L M I L O R E W L T F

N R E E Y R L R A H T N U T A

O A R V B Y R O C C U S N L Y

M C W R A S V H C M R O G E E

I H O U S E L E E K R U W S L

R C R S F M L B E F R O O V R

G G T H A R M C F H U P R G A

A A A E F L E A W O R T T C B

G C H S U B S P S S O L G U B

◊ AGRIMONY
◊ ALEHOOF
◊ AVENS
◊ BARLEY
◊ BISTORT
◊ BRIONY
◊ BUGLOSS
◊ CARROTS
◊ CLEAVERS
◊ ELM TREE
◊ FENNEL
◊ FLEAWORT
◊ HEMLOCK
◊ HEMP
◊ HOUSELEEK
◊ KNAPWEED
◊ LUNGWORT
◊ MOTHERWORT
◊ NETTLES
◊ RHUBARB
◊ RUSHES
◊ SAFFRON
◊ SAGE
◊ SUCCORY

100

Famous People with Plant-Derived Names

```
E N R O H T W A H E L E F B C
R L D R B O X C Y S L L A T T
E E U R L L N G A O U I I E C
A S D L S B S A F R E S A L H
S L I N I L I V T M O H H O Y
Y W L R E A A E U I I W M I T
S N C E I V U U R R R A A V F
I H M W G F A C R P B A Y N Y
A N L Y O I T L R E H T A E H
D O R S T A N N D H L H B U L
Y D E E R N F H A P G S R Y D
A P T C F T L L Y L T U Y L F
I W P C F O R E S T P B O L B
B L O O M F B E P O F H N O A
O U E V P F H E E N I P Y H M
```

◊ VIOLET AFFLECK
◊ IRIS APFEL
◊ ROWAN ATKINSON
◊ THORA BIRCH
◊ ORLANDO BLOOM
◊ GEORGE W. BUSH
◊ POPPY DELEVINGNE
◊ BRYONY HANNAH
◊ NATHANIEL HAWTHORNE
◊ BUDDY HOLLY
◊ FERN KINNEY
◊ STAN LAUREL
◊ NIGELLA LAWSON
◊ DANIELA LAVENDER
◊ HEATHER LOCKLEAR
◊ CHRIS PINE
◊ ROBERT PLANT
◊ NEIL PRIMROSE
◊ NIKKI REED
◊ DAISY RIDLEY
◊ TREE ROLLINS
◊ WILLOW SMITH
◊ LILY TOMLIN
◊ FOREST WHITAKER

101 Places with Plant-Based Names

◊ AZALEA (USA)
◊ BEECH (USA)
◊ BELLFLOWER (USA)
◊ BIRCH TREE (USA)
◊ CYPRESS HILLS (CAN)
◊ DAISY HILL (AUS)
◊ ELM (GBR)
◊ FOHREN-LINDEN (DEU)
◊ FOREST (AUS)
◊ HEATHER (GBR)
◊ HONEYSUCKLE (AUS)
◊ IVY (USA)
◊ LAUREL (USA)
◊ LILY (USA)
◊ MAPLE (CAN)
◊ MYRTLE (USA)
◊ OAKLAND (USA)
◊ OAKLEIGH (AUS)
◊ PALMS (USA)
◊ PINE BLUFF (USA)
◊ RED WILLOW (CAN)
◊ REDWOOD (NZL)
◊ SUNFLOWER (USA)
◊ THISTLE (USA)

Plant-Derived Girls' Names

E	T	A	S	S	A	I	L	L	E	M	A	C	E	R
F	L	E	U	R	T	I	P	B	H	A	C	I	R	E
R	A	L	L	R	A	X	D	T	L	C	Y	H	C	T
M	N	A	Y	O	U	L	N	S	D	O	A	S	A	S
A	L	Z	J	R	I	I	P	T	B	N	D	H	P	A
I	E	A	G	P	C	V	Y	S	I	A	D	W	U	L
N	S	F	R	A	N	J	A	S	M	I	N	E	E	E
U	O	M	Y	Y	G	M	E	N	P	R	F	I	P	N
T	R	H	I	S	W	Y	T	L	E	Z	A	H	W	G
E	M	P	E	N	A	R	C	I	S	S	A	H	I	D
P	I	F	O	A	A	T	H	U	D	M	L	O	L	A
J	R	J	Y	P	H	L	F	L	O	R	A	L	L	H
X	P	G	L	R	P	E	I	M	E	D	S	L	O	L
D	U	F	I	A	R	Y	J	E	B	U	V	Y	W	I
L	A	R	E	D	N	E	V	A	L	G	E	L	H	A

◊ ANISE
◊ ASTER
◊ AYGUL
◊ AZALEA
◊ BLODWEN
◊ CAMELLIA
◊ DAHLIA
◊ DAISY
◊ ERICA
◊ FLEUR
◊ FLORA
◊ HAZEL
◊ HOLLY
◊ HYACINTH
◊ JASMINE
◊ LAVENDER
◊ LEILANI
◊ MYRTLE
◊ NARCISSA
◊ PETUNIA
◊ POPPY
◊ PRIMROSE
◊ VIOLET
◊ WILLOW

103 Trees of Asia (Common Names)

```
E V A L E D N A M O R O C T A
N E E R G F A O S Y S C L K J
S I S N A M R E A I B H A L A
A O V S A I R E S H A R I A S
K R N A N I S G U L N N I M E
H T E D S E R T O I J R L E A
A F A A N S A E K R H S Y S W
L I S I W N N A B E U J C E C
I B H E I A R V L I A C H N O
N C E V E A I W T R S B E A C
D T A R M L E B B E C K E W O
Y R O W P A R M I N F A U I N
G K Y C D O O W K N I T S A U
M E A N A Y A L A M I H J T T
N O M M O C R I A S A C E R A
```

◊ ASIAN HAZEL
◊ BANJH OAK
◊ BHUTAN WHITE PINE
◊ CHINESE PARASOL TREE
◊ COCONUT PALM
◊ COMMON HAWTHORN
◊ COROMANDEL EBONY
◊ ERMAN'S BIRCH
◊ GREEN ALDER
◊ HIMALAYAN MAPLE
◊ KARNIKARA TREE
◊ KOREAN MAPLE
◊ KOUSA
◊ LEBBECK
◊ LYCHEE
◊ MORINDA SPRUCE
◊ OSHIMA CHERRY
◊ SAKHALIN FIR
◊ SAVIN JUNIPER
◊ SIBERIAN FIR
◊ STINKWOOD
◊ SWEET OSMANTHUS
◊ TAIWANESE PHOTINIA
◊ UTIS

104

Tropical and Rainforest Plants (Common Names)

F	E	R	C	T	M	L	V	C	I	A	H	S	E	R
C	A	N	N	O	N	B	A	L	L	N	S	A	U	C
N	W	T	N	W	A	S	T	L	Y	I	G	P	E	T
E	C	K	T	D	S	C	I	C	W	K	A	M	A	I
S	E	P	L	A	A	N	A	S	R	Y	A	J	I	U
Y	S	A	V	A	A	R	D	C	U	K	B	P	S	R
C	H	A	I	V	G	U	K	M	B	L	R	C	O	F
G	M	E	A	U	R	G	S	R	B	I	A	X	E	K
N	U	C	N	I	M	C	E	V	E	S	Z	O	S	C
I	I	C	A	E	K	A	N	S	R	D	I	B	P	A
K	N	N	I	M	R	Y	T	E	G	A	L	D	R	J
L	D	I	L	R	M	A	R	K	R	A	N	N	O	P
A	I	R	E	H	C	T	I	P	O	F	U	A	C	E
W	A	N	O	Z	A	M	A	P	L	P	T	S	R	F
E	N	R	O	H	G	A	T	S	M	A	R	I	P	A

- ◊ AMAZON WATER LILY
- ◊ BRAZIL NUT
- ◊ CACAO TREE
- ◊ CANNONBALL TREE
- ◊ CASSAVA
- ◊ CORPSE LILY
- ◊ DARK RED MERANTI
- ◊ DURIAN
- ◊ INDIAN TIMBER BAMBOO
- ◊ JACKFRUIT
- ◊ KAPOK
- ◊ LIANA
- ◊ MARIPA PALM
- ◊ MONKEY BRUSH VINE
- ◊ PITCHER PLANT
- ◊ POKTAMUI
- ◊ RUBBER TREE
- ◊ SANDBOX TREE
- ◊ SILKY OAK
- ◊ SNAKE PLANT
- ◊ STAGHORN FERN
- ◊ SWISS CHEESE PLANT
- ◊ VANILLA ORCHID
- ◊ WALKING PALM

105 Genera in the Family: Asteraceae – Part Three (Daisy Family)

A M A S U N E D A I L I H C B
I E R D I G I T A C A L I A M
R R E X G U A R D I O L A M W
U P I E E B S J G Y O D E H N
B B N T H I S E L T O N I A W
D A I W X A T I U O A O B I X
A F A I E S I X L H Y A H N F
R U R P Y D A B P O J D U E P
B T P H I A E E Y A X W B S I
U I C R E C T L C R F E E O C
Y A I D H S R A I S U F R R R
P J D L O G L I J A V E T U O
J E U I S I R E S O N O I E S
F A U J A S I A U Y U W A I I
M O S G S U P P A P O X Y M A

◊ *BAFUTIA*
◊ *BAJACALIA*
◊ *BRADBURIA*
◊ *CHILIADENUS*
◊ *DIGITACALIA*
◊ *EURYBIA*
◊ *FAUJASIA*
◊ *FEDDEA*
◊ *GUARDIOLA*
◊ *HUBERTIA*
◊ *IOSTEPHANE*
◊ *MYXOPAPPUS*
◊ *ONOSERIS*
◊ *PACHYSTEGIA*
◊ *PICRIS*
◊ *PICROSIA*
◊ *RAINIERA*
◊ *ROSENIA*
◊ *SILOXERUS*
◊ *THISELTONIA*
◊ *TRIXIS*
◊ *WEDELIA*

106 Branches of Study Related to Botany

```
T Y C A D E Y S C I T E N E G
Y E G P S G Y G O L O N E H P
G B N O M T N F O R E S T R Y
O E R I L T R I E L O G Y E N
L R P Y R O Y O D Y O Y T Y A
O E Y G R A N G B E G T M S T
C S G O N F M Y O O E O Y T O
Y G O L O T A B L L T R M C B
H L L O V E S O L A O A B U O
P R O M N B D X N F P Y N E N
B A C O H O P A T A C N R Y H
E N Y P H Y M O N O X A T B T
O J M R L O I E C O L O G Y E
Y N A T O B O E L A P I J C G
Y G O L O C I M O N O C E G Y
```

- ◊ ASTROBOTANY
- ◊ BATOLOGY
- ◊ BRYOLOGY
- ◊ ECONOMIC BOTANY
- ◊ ETHNOBOTANY
- ◊ FORESTRY
- ◊ MARINE BOTANY
- ◊ MYCOLOGY
- ◊ PALEOBOTANY
- ◊ PALYNOLOGY
- ◊ PHENOLOGY
- ◊ PHYCOLOGY
- ◊ PLANT ANATOMY
- ◊ PLANT BREEDING
- ◊ PLANT CYTOLOGY
- ◊ PLANT ECOLOGY
- ◊ PLANT GENETICS
- ◊ PLANT TAXONOMY
- ◊ POMOLOGY
- ◊ RHODOLOGY

107 Leaf Shapes and Arrangements

```
F E Y A M C U N E A T E E E S
A B E D A B L O B E D S T R A
N B I M E L A C I C U L A R R
E F D P I L U S N T E E I E R
C G L N I A T A B T E S X T E
T I E A R N E O A D T R P A E
E A T I B C N D I A A E E I T
R S E P T E R A T D T N R L A
N E T E I O L E T A S I F O N
A T A L C L Y L D E A F O F N
T A M T P A L E A G H O L I I
E V L A A T P E P T G R I N P
I O A T T E S A Y B E M A U I
S B P E N A C U M I N A T E R
E O R A L U C I B R O Y E R T
```

- ◊ ACICULAR
- ◊ ACUMINATE
- ◊ ARISTATE
- ◊ BIPINNATE
- ◊ CORDATE
- ◊ CUNEATE
- ◊ DELTOID
- ◊ ELLIPTIC
- ◊ FLABELLATE
- ◊ HASTATE
- ◊ LANCEOLATE
- ◊ LINEAR
- ◊ LOBED
- ◊ OBOVATE
- ◊ OBTUSE
- ◊ ORBICULAR
- ◊ PALMATE
- ◊ PEDATE
- ◊ PELTATE
- ◊ PERFOLIATE
- ◊ RENIFORM
- ◊ TERNATE
- ◊ TRIPINNATE
- ◊ UNIFOLIATE

Plants in *The Complete Herbal* by Nicholas Culpeper – Part Three

M	G	E	R	M	A	N	D	E	R	D	V	E	O	O
A	L	V	V	B	O	F	S	P	F	R	O	L	S	D
S	O	I	N	Y	U	O	C	M	F	M	B	C	N	W
T	V	D	S	I	R	T	A	O	S	R	U	I	K	A
E	A	N	T	R	G	R	T	I	N	R	A	N	N	S
R	G	E	E	D	I	H	W	E	V	I	U	A	I	A
W	E	L	L	G	N	U	T	Y	R	S	O	S	A	R
O	N	S	O	T	T	O	G	S	A	B	E	N	L	A
R	Y	L	I	V	R	R	I	M	H	S	U	B	S	B
T	D	E	V	Y	A	O	O	L	U	A	E	R	R	A
S	C	E	L	S	U	T	W	W	E	L	D	R	U	C
W	L	C	S	S	J	S	R	G	G	D	L	E	P	C
A	B	A	Y	T	R	E	E	V	I	A	N	E	O	A
N	R	O	H	T	W	A	H	C	X	F	R	A	I	F
Y	R	F	M	O	C	F	P	N	X	W	O	A	D	N

◊ ASARABACCA
◊ BAY-TREE
◊ BUTTER-BUR
◊ COMFRY
◊ DANDELION
◊ DOCK
◊ ENDIVE
◊ FIGWORT
◊ GERMANDER
◊ HAWTHORN
◊ LOVAGE
◊ MARIGOLDS
◊ MASTERWORT
◊ MULLEIN
◊ NIGHTSHADE
◊ ONIONS
◊ PARSLEY
◊ PURSLAIN
◊ RAGWORT
◊ SANICLE
◊ SCURVYGRASS
◊ SORREL
◊ VIOLETS
◊ WOAD

109 Genera in the Family: Brassicaceae – Part Two (Cabbage Family)

- ◊ *ALYSSUM*
- ◊ *APLANODES*
- ◊ *ARABIS*
- ◊ *ASTA*
- ◊ *BERTEROELLA*
- ◊ *CAKILE*
- ◊ *CAMELINA*
- ◊ *EIGIA*
- ◊ *ERYSIMUM*
- ◊ *EUCLIDIUM*
- ◊ *GOERKEMIA*
- ◊ *GRAELLSIA*
- ◊ *LEPTALEUM*
- ◊ *LITWINOWIA*
- ◊ *MALCOLMIA*
- ◊ *MICROTHLASPI*
- ◊ *NASTURTIOPSIS*
- ◊ *SELENIA*
- ◊ *SIBAROPSIS*
- ◊ *ZUVANDA*

110 Cacti (Common Names)

```
N A I V U R E P F O X T A I L
A Y H O R S E C R I P P L E R
N O O M P R E G N I F Y D A L
A F R I C A N P B A P E Y N S
F P E R U V E E I R V H A A L
N E M A N Y E R I I V G M A N
B B A V O H Y C L N R T J U E
R U H T I Y K S T O S U S T T
N N E V H L H O R I M G A A I
Y N E Y Y E L R R P B N N R A
L Y O M A D R H I A E Y P I M
O E O D M I C N R R I M E Z E
N A N A T N G R C J M L D O L
U R N P X W E H E F D M R N O
U S O L D L A D Y T N W O A N
```

- ◊ AFRICAN MILK TREE
- ◊ ARIZONA RAINBOW CACTUS
- ◊ BARREL CACTUS
- ◊ BEEHIVE CACTUS
- ◊ BUNNY EARS CACTUS
- ◊ CHRISTMAS CACTUS
- ◊ CRENATE ORCHID CACTUS
- ◊ DEVILSHEAD
- ◊ FAIRY CASTLE CACTUS
- ◊ FEATHER CACTUS
- ◊ FOXTAIL CACTUS
- ◊ HORSE CRIPPLER
- ◊ JUMPING CHOLLA
- ◊ LADYFINGER CACTUS
- ◊ MELON CACTUS
- ◊ MOON CACTUS
- ◊ NYLON HEDGEHOG CACTUS
- ◊ OLD LADY CACTUS
- ◊ OLD MAN CACTUS
- ◊ ORGAN PIPE CACTUS
- ◊ PERUVIAN APPLE CACTUS
- ◊ PEYOTE
- ◊ PRICKLY PEAR
- ◊ SAN PEDRO CACTUS

111 Plant Families Beginning with C

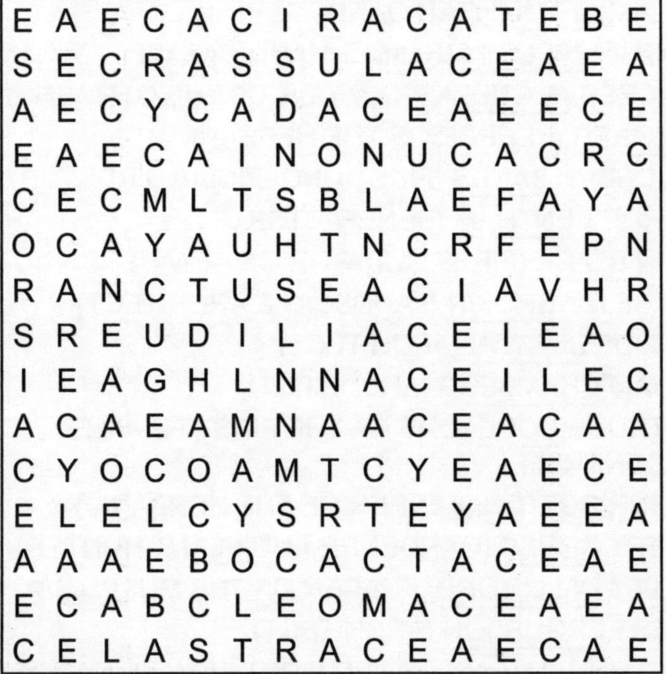

- ◊ *CACTACEAE*
- ◊ *CALOMNIACEAE*
- ◊ *CALYCERACEAE*
- ◊ *CANELLACEAE*
- ◊ *CANNACEAE*
- ◊ *CARICACEAE*
- ◊ *CELASTRACEAE*
- ◊ *CISTACEAE*
- ◊ *CLEOMACEAE*
- ◊ *CLEVEACEAE*
- ◊ *CLUSIACEAE*
- ◊ *CORNACEAE*
- ◊ *CORSIACEAE*
- ◊ *COSTACEAE*
- ◊ *CRASSULACEAE*
- ◊ *CRYPHAEACEAE*
- ◊ *CUNONIACEAE*
- ◊ *CYATHEACEAE*
- ◊ *CYCADACEAE*
- ◊ *CYTINACEAE*

- ◊ WILLIAM AITON (HEAD GARDENER)
- ◊ GEORGE APPLEBY (STABLE HAND/CARTER)
- ◊ PRINCESS AUGUSTA (FOUNDER OF THE GARDENS)
- ◊ J.G. BAKER (KEEPER OF THE HERBARIUM)
- ◊ SIR JOSEPH BANKS (FIRST UNOFFICIAL DIRECTOR)
- ◊ GEORGE BENTHAM (BENEFACTOR)
- ◊ ALLAN BLACK (FIRST CURATOR OF KEW HERBARIUM)
- ◊ CAPABILITY BROWN (LANDSCAPE ARCHITECT)
- ◊ DECIMUS BURTON (ARCHITECT)
- ◊ WILLIAM CHAMBERS (ARCHITECT)
- ◊ GERTRUDE COPE (ONE OF THE FIRST FEMALE GARDENERS)
- ◊ ARTHUR COTTON (KEEPER OF THE HERBARIUM)
- ◊ ROBERT CROSS (GARDENER AND PLANT HUNTER)
- ◊ WILLIAM DALLIMORE (KEEPER OF THE MUSEUMS)
- ◊ JAMES FERGUSSON (ARCHITECT)
- ◊ ANNIE GULVIN (ONE OF THE FIRST FEMALE GARDENERS)
- ◊ ARTHUR HILL (DIRECTOR)
- ◊ WILLIAM HOOKER (DIRECTOR)
- ◊ ALICE HUTCHINGS (ONE OF THE FIRST FEMALE GARDENERS)
- ◊ JOHN HUTCHINSON (KEEPER OF THE MUSEUMS)
- ◊ FRANCIS MASSON (FIRST PLANT HUNTER)
- ◊ ELEANOR MORLAND (ONE OF THE FIRST FEMALE GARDENERS)
- ◊ WILLIAM NESFIELD (LANDSCAPE ARCHITECT)
- ◊ MARIANNE NORTH (BOTANICAL ARTIST AND BENEFACTOR)
- ◊ DANIEL OLIVER (KEEPER OF THE HERBARIUM)
- ◊ JOHN SMITH (FIRST CURATOR)
- ◊ OTTO STAPF (KEEPER OF THE HERBARIUM)
- ◊ WILLIAM THISELTON-DYER (DIRECTOR)
- ◊ RICHARD TURNER (ENGINEER)
- ◊ WILLIAM BERTRAM TURRILL (KEEPER OF THE HERBARIUM AND LIBRARY)
- ◊ ERNEST WILSON (PLANT HUNTER)

A	R	A	I	T	O	N	T	U	R	E	N	R	U	T
N	H	U	T	C	H	I	N	S	O	N	O	R	T	H
M	O	S	S	S	R	E	B	M	A	H	C	H	R	B
O	O	T	H	I	S	E	L	T	O	N	D	Y	E	R
R	K	C	T	F	B	E	S	K	N	A	B	U	V	O
L	E	P	I	O	D	U	R	S	T	A	P	F	I	W
A	R	E	U	F	C	W	R	O	T	Y	N	E	L	N
N	L	C	R	O	S	S	I	T	M	L	E	H	O	I
D	M	T	U	R	R	I	L	L	O	I	M	I	U	R
V	E	A	U	G	U	S	T	A	S	N	L	L	I	A
A	Y	T	S	S	I	L	S	O	N	O	M	L	K	S
F	T	N	O	S	S	U	G	R	E	F	N	C	A	C
S	M	I	T	H	O	B	E	N	T	H	A	M	O	D
N	I	V	L	U	G	N	Y	B	E	L	P	P	A	T
S	G	N	I	H	C	T	U	H	B	R	E	K	A	B

113 Excerpt – *Kew Gardens with the Pleasure Grounds and Park: A Handbook Guide for Visitors (Fifth Edition 1852)*

No more delightful day's pleasure can be spent in the neighbourhood of the metropolis, than that which is afforded a holiday at Kew. Formerly it was deemed a place of vulgar resort, and strange to say, it was at that period but little frequented; but now, all classes, almost from the peer to the peasant, are accustomed to visit it, and yet it is considered equally agreeable and select … A stranger desirous of passing a day at Kew, may do so without in any degree infringing the principles of economy. For the small sum of eightpence he may secure his passage up and down by a day ticket on the South Western Railroad, or for the matter of sevenpence he may go or return, if he wish to vary the route, by an agreeable passage on the Thames … By whatever route the visitor from the metropolis arrives in Kew, he can scarcely avoid traversing its bridge, and we should recommend him to pause for some moments on its centre, and admire the beautiful views on either side, before he quits a spot of such enchantment.

114 Botanical Terms – Part Three

R	E	W	O	L	F	A	N	T	R	E	S	A	I	Z
E	R	G	H	E	R	T	O	O	R	P	A	T	O	A
A	C	P	O	R	B	I	C	U	L	A	R	N	R	C
Y	B	M	J	H	I	L	U	M	W	P	A	C	G	E
E	W	A	R	T	Y	M	P	M	G	T	F	I	G	H
E	L	R	X	A	M	D	U	U	E	I	G	S	Y	T
T	S	U	C	I	O	R	L	I	L	S	N	E	Y	M
A	A	V	G	L	A	U	E	D	E	U	S	M	A	A
N	M	X	P	A	I	L	O	I	B	O	N	R	E	Y
O	C	O	O	W	P	N	D	S	M	C	G	R	H	E
R	A	T	N	N	F	O	E	I	U	I	C	B	B	S
C	L	I	C	O	R	E	R	Y	N	O	I	H	A	R
U	Y	S	H	A	C	H	M	P	B	I	V	U	M	E
M	X	A	B	Y	R	O	N	U	M	D	E	F	U	M
G	R	E	T	E	I	B	T	P	I	N	N	A	T	E

◊ ABAXIAL
◊ BRACT
◊ CALYX
◊ CLINE
◊ CUPULE
◊ DIOICOUS
◊ FLOWER
◊ HILUM
◊ ISIDIUM
◊ MARGIN
◊ MESIC
◊ MONOCOT
◊ MUCRONATE
◊ OCREA
◊ ORBICULAR
◊ PINNATE
◊ PROPAGULE
◊ RIMOSE
◊ TAPROOT
◊ TAXON
◊ THECA
◊ UMBEL
◊ WARTY
◊ ZONATE

115

Animals in Plant Names (Common Names)

```
D E A T R E D I P S I F R O G
O S W A L C R E T S B O L R M
G Y I O O R A G N A K I B T L
T E H R A B B I T B R U S H A
O K X A N D R U C P F L N Y N
O N R A W P R O T F I E S K I
T O F E S K S A A T L N V O D
H M I R G T W L E A E L T E R
B I A R R I O E M B S R S A A
S E R I B A T B E P S N F O C
B P C D E D S U E D O T X L S
G H O R S E R A D I S H A S Y
E V O L G X O F L P A R R O T
P A R T R I D G E T O Y O C G
R R O I L G O O S E B E R R Y
```

◊ BEAR'S BREECHES
◊ BUFFALO GOURD
◊ BUTTERFLY BUSH
◊ CARDINAL FLOWER
◊ CATNIP
◊ COYOTE MELON
◊ DOGTOOTH VIOLET
◊ FOXGLOVE
◊ GOATSBEARD
◊ GOOSEBERRY
◊ HAWKWEED
◊ HORSERADISH
◊ KANGAROO PAW
◊ LAMB'S EAR
◊ LION'S TAIL
◊ LOBSTER-CLAWS
◊ MONKEY FACE ORCHID
◊ OSTRICH FERN
◊ PARROT FLOWER
◊ PARTRIDGE PEA
◊ RABBITBRUSH
◊ SKUNK CABBAGE
◊ SPIDER PLANT
◊ TIGER LILY

116

Trees of North America (Common Names)

F	R	A	W	D	T	U	N	T	S	E	H	C	U	C
A	K	T	O	O	N	G	G	I	V	E	S	Y	F	I
I	R	O	N	O	A	H	F	A	A	S	N	A	H	F
G	Y	Y	K	C	U	T	N	E	K	T	E	R	E	I
Y	R	N	V	R	Y	U	H	C	L	L	N	A	Q	C
N	L	A	R	A	D	Y	E	G	E	L	V	U	P	A
A	I	B	B	O	E	M	W	L	I	B	A	H	O	P
C	D	D	U	L	H	N	T	H	Y	K	G	S	P	M
I	E	B	L	C	R	T	N	T	I	W	P	O	C	A
R	Y	O	A	E	I	O	E	N	K	T	R	J	S	C
E	W	M	T	L	P	X	G	H	U	C	E	E	O	Y
M	S	S	A	U	A	D	M	P	C	B	A	A	K	S
A	E	L	A	S	G	S	E	S	W	T	S	L	O	T
W	R	Y	A	E	R	L	K	V	R	T	I	M	B	E
H	E	N	Y	F	O	G	A	A	H	S	F	P	V	P

◊ ALASKA BIRCH
◊ AMERICAN HORNBEAM
◊ BLACK ASH
◊ CHESTNUT OAK
◊ COAST REDWOOD
◊ DWARF MAPLE
◊ FALSE MASTIC
◊ JOSHUA TREE
◊ KENTUCKY COFFEETREE
◊ LITTLELEAF SUMAC
◊ MOUNTAIN SILVERBELL
◊ NOOTKA CYPRESS
◊ PACIFIC DOGWOOD
◊ PITCH PINE
◊ QUAKING ASPEN
◊ RED BAY
◊ SILKY DOGWOOD
◊ TEXAS EBONY
◊ THORNY LOCUST
◊ TUPELO
◊ WESTERN JUNIPER
◊ WHITE SPRUCE
◊ YAUPON HOLLY
◊ YELLOW BUCKEYE

117 Succulents (Common Names)

- ◊ ALOE VERA
- ◊ BARREL CACTUS
- ◊ BEAR'S PAW
- ◊ BOTTLE CACTUS
- ◊ BURRO'S TAIL
- ◊ CAMPFIRE PLANT
- ◊ CHALK LETTUCE
- ◊ CHRIST PLANT
- ◊ COAST DUDLEYA
- ◊ ELEPHANT BUSH
- ◊ GHOST PLANT
- ◊ HENS AND CHICKS
- ◊ JELLY BEAN PLANT
- ◊ JEWEL-LEAF PLANT
- ◊ LACE ALOE
- ◊ LIMESTONE LIVEFOREVER
- ◊ LIVING STONES
- ◊ MADAGASCAR OCOTILLO
- ◊ PANDA PLANT
- ◊ PROPELLER PLANT
- ◊ RATTAIL CRASSULA
- ◊ STICKS ON FIRE
- ◊ STRING OF HEARTS
- ◊ ZEBRA PLANT

118 Genera in the Family: Myrtaceae – Part Three (Myrtle Family)

- ◊ *ALGRIZEA*
- ◊ *ALUTA*
- ◊ *BARONGIA*
- ◊ *BASISPERMA*
- ◊ *CURITIBA*
- ◊ *DARWINIA*
- ◊ *GOMIDESIA*
- ◊ *HARMOGIA*
- ◊ *KARDOMIA*
- ◊ *LITHOMYRTUS*
- ◊ *LUMA*
- ◊ *MARLIEREA*
- ◊ *MYRTELLA*
- ◊ *PILIOCALYX*
- ◊ *PIMENTA*
- ◊ *REGELIA*
- ◊ *RISTANTIA*
- ◊ *SYNCARPIA*
- ◊ *SYZYGIUM*
- ◊ *TRIPLARINA*
- ◊ *TRISTANIA*
- ◊ *UGNI*

119 Female Botanists – Part Two

O	M	J	W	N	O	R	L	A	D	R	O	N	O	N
J	A	Y	E	A	F	F	A	H	G	E	R	R	B	D
U	A	O	I	R	U	R	I	B	S	G	E	N	H	U
Y	T	C	K	G	N	D	E	S	P	I	T	R	X	K
R	E	T	S	E	K	N	A	L	O	O	B	I	E	H
S	E	P	R	O	C	C	I	T	G	C	Y	R	E	Q
A	M	S	E	F	N	D	H	L	N	E	A	M	U	P
E	H	N	Y	T	G	O	R	H	E	U	P	I	A	F
I	N	E	A	E	D	L	T	A	D	E	R	B	S	T
R	B	N	U	G	L	X	A	R	L	K	H	T	Z	T
H	W	R	S	C	N	H	E	K	O	L	O	I	T	E
T	H	O	E	I	R	N	R	U	C	N	U	X	R	C
U	N	B	E	W	R	I	T	L	E	U	N	B	E	W
G	V	S	E	S	I	U	B	L	A	B	U	E	P	A
C	F	O	N	O	S	S	O	B	R	I	G	G	S	F

◊ ANNE BREWIS
◊ BARBARA G. BRIGGS
◊ ELAINE BULLARD
◊ JANE COLDEN
◊ JOAN CRIBB
◊ EDNA H. FAWCETT
◊ VICKI FUNK
◊ CATHERINE FURBISH
◊ LOUISE GUTHRIE
◊ JENNY HEMPEL
◊ AMY HODGSON
◊ MARIA ELIZABETHA JACSON
◊ MONIQUE KERAUDREN
◊ RUTH KIEW
◊ TIIU KULL
◊ PHOEBE LANKESTER
◊ OTTOLINE LEYSER
◊ INGER NORDAL
◊ DAPHNE OSBORNE
◊ ALICE PEGLER
◊ DOROTHEA PERTZ
◊ AGNES J. QUIRK
◊ ILMA GRACE STONE
◊ MARY TREAT

120 Trees of South America (Common Names)

```
N R O T N A S O L A P M O L L
E H C I R O M N R R J L T A L
D W M A L A B A R R E M O D A
L H A C P G X C N N E B L A U
O I C E D R O I C V U F B R Q
G T T A L A M A N C A S U U U
O E L J W O O M A K H P E A R
A B R A Z I L A U O H E C N P
X O B D N A S J R P N C H D E
M A B H I E U T I A T D M E Y
O Y B Q U A L J V K C B L A S
N V A E B E I W P T J W I N H
K L L U A O M O C A M B O R I
E B S F C A N N O N B A L L N
Y V A O S Y L V A W O L L E Y
```

- ◊ ANDEAN OAK
- ◊ BALSA TREE
- ◊ BRAZIL NUT
- ◊ CANNONBALL TREE
- ◊ CEDRO
- ◊ GOLDEN TRUMPET TREE
- ◊ JAMAICAN CAPER
- ◊ KAPOK
- ◊ MALABAR CHESTNUT
- ◊ MOCAMBO TREE
- ◊ MONKEY PUZZLE
- ◊ MORICHE PALM
- ◊ PALO SANTO
- ◊ PAU FERRO
- ◊ PIJIO
- ◊ QUEEN PALM
- ◊ RADAL
- ◊ RUBBER TREE
- ◊ SANDBOX TREE
- ◊ SHINY OYSTERWOOD
- ◊ SHORTLEAF FIG
- ◊ TALAMANCA OAK
- ◊ WHITE QUEBRACHO
- ◊ YELLOW LAPACHO

121 Cottage Garden Plants (Common Names)

M	U	I	N	I	H	P	L	E	D	A	R	I	K	U
Y	D	F	O	X	G	L	O	V	E	P	S	L	C	F
U	N	H	E	M	O	C	D	F	O	U	O	O	O	S
Y	M	O	R	S	U	L	A	B	H	N	O	I	H	E
S	S	O	E	L	M	I	H	T	D	E	A	D	Y	U
W	S	I	L	P	M	U	N	P	M	R	E	A	L	G
E	B	V	A	L	A	A	I	E	B	I	E	L	L	N
E	E	D	A	D	I	I	T	N	L	N	N	G	O	O
T	G	A	R	D	A	S	R	P	A	E	P	T	H	T
P	O	L	I	A	N	T	H	E	S	R	H	D	W	D
E	N	E	N	E	A	F	S	A	T	L	E	P	E	R
A	I	A	I	L	H	A	D	A	U	S	O	G	S	A
L	A	V	E	N	D	E	R	P	H	P	I	I	E	E
A	Q	U	I	L	E	G	I	A	P	S	D	W	V	B
U	L	O	X	I	N	N	W	Y	C	O	S	M	O	S

◊ AQUILEGIA
◊ BEARDTONGUES
◊ BEGONIA
◊ CATMINT
◊ COSMOS
◊ DAHLIA
◊ DELPHINIUM
◊ DIANTHUS
◊ FOXGLOVE
◊ GERANIUMS
◊ GLADIOLI
◊ HELENIUM
◊ HOLLYHOCK
◊ LAVENDER
◊ LUPIN
◊ NERINE
◊ PEONY
◊ PHLOX
◊ POLIANTHES
◊ POPPY
◊ ROSE
◊ SHASTA DAISY
◊ SWEET PEA
◊ WISTERIA

122 Spring Flowers (Common Names)

E	N	X	H	C	Y	A	G	Y	B	J	Y	M	S	C
A	T	R	A	C	B	N	I	T	R	G	T	U	P	U
X	E	L	E	N	T	L	O	L	A	L	L	I	C	S
L	I	L	V	T	E	I	U	E	L	I	A	L	C	B
L	H	R	A	E	S	M	W	E	P	E	O	L	H	L
I	L	E	I	Z	P	A	O	L	B	R	M	A	Y	O
S	I	E	L	S	A	L	E	N	Y	E	P	A	A	O
F	C	A	R	L	R	A	T	S	E	U	L	B	C	D
S	A	L	I	G	E	U	T	E	O	N	X	L	I	R
N	S	L	W	S	V	B	V	C	W	R	R	J	N	O
A	Y	D	W	T	E	N	O	I	R	V	M	S	T	O
K	L	N	V	W	G	E	N	R	E	O	F	I	H	T
E	N	P	I	L	U	T	R	T	E	E	C	V	R	A
S	P	I	R	A	E	A	P	F	N	R	Y	U	L	P
A	C	F	O	R	S	Y	T	H	I	A	L	X	S	O

- ◊ ALLIUM
- ◊ ANEMONE
- ◊ AZALEA
- ◊ BLOODROOT
- ◊ BLUEBELL
- ◊ BLUESTAR
- ◊ CAMELLIA
- ◊ CROCUS
- ◊ EASTERN REDBUD
- ◊ FORSYTHIA
- ◊ FREESIA
- ◊ HELLEBORE
- ◊ HYACINTH
- ◊ IRIS
- ◊ LILAC
- ◊ LILY OF THE VALLEY
- ◊ PEONY
- ◊ PRIMROSE
- ◊ SCILLA
- ◊ SNAKES HEAD FRITILLARY
- ◊ SPIRAEA
- ◊ TULIP
- ◊ WINTER ACONITE
- ◊ WITCH HAZEL

123 Only-Known Species in the Genera – Part Two (Common Names)

N	D	E	N	T	R	I	O	S	P	Y	L	A	C	C
T	U	N	O	C	O	C	A	E	S	L	C	A	S	N
A	N	A	A	M	R	J	G	F	A	N	V	R	A	L
M	E	N	A	L	U	H	A	M	A	S	D	C	E	L
E	A	R	O	Y	O	E	S	M	E	C	N	A	A	W
U	S	D	E	T	L	D	R	P	D	J	U	E	N	U
H	S	W	R	A	R	E	N	F	W	N	O	T	I	V
I	R	I	N	O	G	E	R	O	T	V	R	I	D	I
P	G	N	D	C	C	U	H	L	P	I	G	H	N	R
O	A	G	B	E	I	K	U	T	M	O	B	W	A	G
C	A	E	E	B	S	C	R	F	A	L	S	E	N	I
P	I	D	A	W	Y	E	J	O	V	E	C	V	P	N
M	S	F	C	W	S	B	R	P	O	T	A	B	D	I
F	I	S	H	T	A	I	L	T	E	T	P	L	A	A
C	A	M	P	B	E	L	L	S	Y	P	E	R	E	R

- ◊ ATHERTON OAK
- ◊ AUNT LUCY
- ◊ BEACH FESCUE
- ◊ CALYPSO ORCHID
- ◊ CAMPBELL'S LIVERWORT
- ◊ CANNALEAF MYROSMA
- ◊ CAPE EDELWEISS
- ◊ COPIHUE
- ◊ DESERT FLUFF-GRASS
- ◊ FALSE ANEMONE
- ◊ FISHTAIL OAK
- ◊ GERMAN MADWORT
- ◊ GROUND PINEAPPLE
- ◊ MARSH ROSE
- ◊ NANDINA
- ◊ OREGON BENSONIELLA
- ◊ PONDOLAND PALM
- ◊ ROCKROOT
- ◊ SEA COCONUT
- ◊ SMALL POVERTYWEED
- ◊ VIOLET DRAPERIA
- ◊ VIRGINIA CHAIN FERN
- ◊ WHITE WARATAH
- ◊ WINGED PIGWEED

Shade Tolerant Plants

P	S	G	E	R	O	B	E	L	L	E	H	M	E	A
C	E	N	L	W	O	D	A	E	M	P	S	A	W	R
O	S	I	E	U	C	A	D	E	R	A	O	O	F	E
P	E	D	S	M	N	S	S	A	M	E	L	F	U	N
P	N	E	O	P	A	G	Y	O	O	G	O	T	E	N
E	A	E	R	O	Y	L	W	D	N	T	M	I	V	U
R	P	L	M	R	M	R	C	O	A	T	O	D	O	R
P	A	B	I	D	D	Y	R	Y	R	L	N	E	L	B
D	J	T	R	W	Y	Y	E	E	C	T	S	M	G	C
P	A	S	P	O	T	T	E	D	B	L	G	I	X	O
B	L	E	D	N	R	U	P	U	A	E	B	U	O	R
L	O	R	D	S	H	V	I	F	M	P	N	E	F	A
P	H	B	A	R	R	E	N	W	O	R	T	A	D	L
Y	A	N	D	E	R	S	G	U	L	H	W	J	B	H
P	L	L	I	B	S	E	N	A	R	C	A	L	Y	T

- ◊ BANEBERRY
- ◊ BARRENWORT
- ◊ BLEEDING HEART
- ◊ BRUNNERA
- ◊ COPPER SHIELD FERN
- ◊ CORAL BELLS
- ◊ CRANESBILL GERANIUM
- ◊ CREEPING JENNY
- ◊ CYCLAMEN
- ◊ DEAD NETTLE
- ◊ FALSE GOAT'S BEARD
- ◊ FOAM FLOWER
- ◊ FOXGLOVE
- ◊ HELLEBORE
- ◊ JAPANESE FOREST GRASS
- ◊ LADY'S MANTLE
- ◊ LORDS AND LADIES
- ◊ LUNGWORT
- ◊ MEADOW RUE
- ◊ PRIMROSE
- ◊ SNOWDROP
- ◊ SOLOMON'S SEAL
- ◊ SPOTTED DEAD-NETTLE
- ◊ TOAD LILY

125 Grasses (Common Names)

V	R	A	L	S	S	A	R	G	R	E	V	L	I	S
B	W	E	C	O	G	O	N	G	R	A	S	S	P	S
A	E	H	V	C	E	N	T	I	P	E	D	E	W	M
H	L	A	E	I	Y	L	I	Y	F	C	A	I	U	R
I	A	R	R	A	T	R	S	A	H	R	T	E	S	D
A	Y	M	A	D	T	E	A	J	T	C	D	S	G	T
G	F	H	I	G	B	S	V	N	H	N	I	T	A	I
R	Y	E	G	R	A	S	S	G	A	A	U	D	V	M
A	C	W	O	C	T	G	R	O	S	C	A	O	N	O
S	A	M	O	S	B	A	H	T	A	I	D	Y	F	T
S	E	U	T	A	S	Y	O	S	P	X	Y	E	E	H
E	C	I	R	S	U	D	D	T	M	E	T	E	E	Y
H	P	L	G	I	H	S	E	S	A	M	W	U	Y	R
B	E	N	T	G	R	A	S	S	P	S	T	I	U	O
Y	B	A	M	B	O	O	C	E	N	O	K	A	H	A

◊ BAHIAGRASS

◊ BAMBOO

◊ BARLEY

◊ BEARD GRASS

◊ BENTGRASS

◊ BROME GRASS

◊ CENTIPEDE GRASS

◊ COGONGRASS

◊ COUCH GRASS

◊ FOUNTAIN GRASS

◊ HAKONE GRASS

◊ MEXICAN FEATHERGRASS

◊ PAMPAS GRASS

◊ REED CANARY GRASS

◊ RHODES GRASS

◊ RICE

◊ RYEGRASS

◊ SILVERGRASS

◊ SPEAR GRASS

◊ SWEET GRASS

◊ SWITCHGRASS

◊ TIMOTHY GRASS

◊ VETIVER

◊ WHEAT

126

Rudyard Kipling – *The Way Through the Woods* (1910)

```
H G U O R H T E C I P P O C E
S E A S E B A D G E R S O J R
T H R A E F M G B R O O D S E
R W U A O D N I I S E E R T H
O S O T U I U N S E C N O N T
U E T O N W G T K T A B I Y S
T E Y E D D E W I M Y G E E E
R S V T O S Y A R L H U S A L
I E U V N R N R T T O U T R T
N S E M E E J S A H A S E S S
G R L W M V V I W C E R A L I
E O E O O E R E E I O R D O H
D H N T S N R B S F S D I O W
W E N K N T K H E A T H L P E
S R E P E E K B D A O R Y O F
```

They shut the road through the woods
Seventy years ago.
Weather and rain have undone it again,
And now you would never know
There was once a road through the woods
Before they planted the trees.
It is underneath the coppice and heath,
And the thin anemones.
Only the keeper sees
That, where the ring-dove broods,
And the badgers roll at ease,
There was once a road through the woods.

Yet, if you enter the woods
Of a summer evening late,
When the night-air cools on the trout-ringed pools
Where the otter whistles his mate,
(They fear not men in the woods,
Because they see so few.)
You will hear the beat of a horse's feet,
And the swish of a skirt in the dew,
Steadily cantering through
The misty solitudes,
As though they perfectly knew
The old lost road through the woods.
But there is no road through the woods.

127

Plant Families with Nine-Letter Names

O	Y	V	E	A	E	C	A	E	M	I	L	E	I	H
E	B	E	N	A	C	E	A	E	C	A	Y	R	O	B
N	H	H	A	T	S	E	A	A	R	U	C	E	A	E
E	T	L	G	E	C	E	D	E	E	U	A	M	A	A
A	A	L	O	A	C	O	R	A	C	E	A	E	E	E
I	N	E	I	A	X	A	E	S	C	A	C	A	A	C
L	U	M	C	A	S	C	N	A	N	A	T	E	E	A
R	A	A	C	A	A	A	C	P	O	J	Y	C	C	N
Z	L	E	B	C	T	N	C	Z	Y	F	P	A	A	H
O	A	W	E	P	U	S	I	E	Y	H	H	T	N	C
E	L	R	F	J	E	A	I	J	A	J	A	R	R	O
E	A	E	C	A	N	N	A	C	W	E	C	Y	O	L
S	A	B	I	A	C	E	A	E	Y	U	E	M	C	A
L	O	W	I	A	C	E	A	E	G	U	A	V	R	E
R	A	S	E	R	M	A	L	V	A	C	E	A	E	A

◊ *ACORACEAE*
◊ *ADOXACEAE*
◊ *AIZOACEAE*
◊ *ARECACEAE*
◊ *BORYACEAE*
◊ *CACTACEAE*
◊ *CANNACEAE*
◊ *CISTACEAE*
◊ *CORNACEAE*
◊ *EBENACEAE*
◊ *HYPNACEAE*
◊ *JUNCACEAE*
◊ *LIMEACEAE*
◊ *LOASACEAE*
◊ *LOWIACEAE*
◊ *MALVACEAE*
◊ *MYRTACEAE*
◊ *OCHNACEAE*
◊ *OLACACEAE*
◊ *SABIACEAE*
◊ *TYPHACEAE*
◊ *ZAMIACEAE*

Mythical and Folk Tale Plants

◊ AGLAOPHOTIS
◊ APPLE TREE MAN
◊ AUSTRAS KOKS
◊ BARNACLE TREE
◊ FERN FLOWER
◊ FUSANG
◊ GOLDEN APPLE OF DISCORD
◊ GREEN MAN
◊ HANTU TINGGI
◊ HUNGRY GRASS
◊ JINMENJU
◊ JUBOKKO
◊ LOTUS TREE
◊ MOLY
◊ MONEY TREE
◊ NARIPHON
◊ RASKOVNIK
◊ SANJEEVANI
◊ SKY-HIGH TREE
◊ TALKING TREES
◊ VAMPIRE PUMPKINS
◊ VEGETABLE LAMB OF TARTARY
◊ WORLD TREE
◊ YGGDRASIL

129 Sun-Loving Plants

```
V E R A C I N O R E V A U A A
S A I P E L C S A E L B I T H
A G A S T A C H E C T S E D A
E U S U C P I D E D I S D B M
L E U C A N T H E M U M A U N
L I A S I A F S E A B M I A I
I D T I R O L T E I A N Y N C
H I E B E L R U A L I P F E O
C A P I M A L O N H H I A B R
A N E H R F D T P A E R I R E
A T N E A N G L V D P E V E O
L H A I K C E B D U R M L V P
C U G L A D I O L U S T A B S
E S V A L U D N A V A L S C I
A I N O E A P P S Y H C A T S
```

- ◊ *ACHILLEA MILLEFOLIUM*
- ◊ *AGASTACHE*
- ◊ *ALCEA*
- ◊ *ARMERIA MARITIMA*
- ◊ *ARTEMISIA*
- ◊ *ASCLEPIAS TUBEROSA*
- ◊ *ASTER*
- ◊ *CAMPANULA*
- ◊ *COREOPSIS*
- ◊ *DAHLIA*
- ◊ *DELPHINIUM*
- ◊ *DIANTHUS*
- ◊ *GLADIOLUS*
- ◊ *HIBISCUS*
- ◊ *LAVANDULA*
- ◊ *LEUCANTHEMUM*
- ◊ *NEPETA CATARIA*
- ◊ *PAEONIA*
- ◊ *RUDBECKIA HIRTA*
- ◊ *SALVIA YANGII*
- ◊ *SEDUM*
- ◊ *STACHYS BYZANTINA*
- ◊ *VERBENA*
- ◊ *VERONICA*

Solutions

1

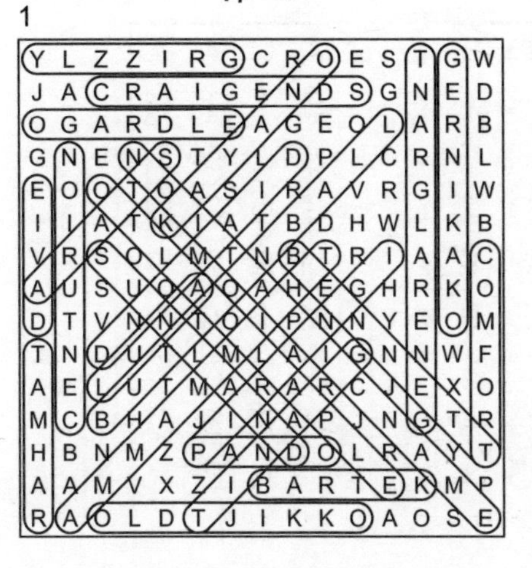

2

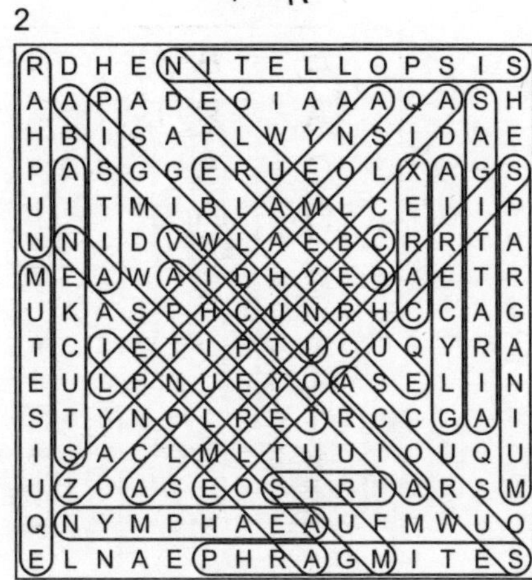

3

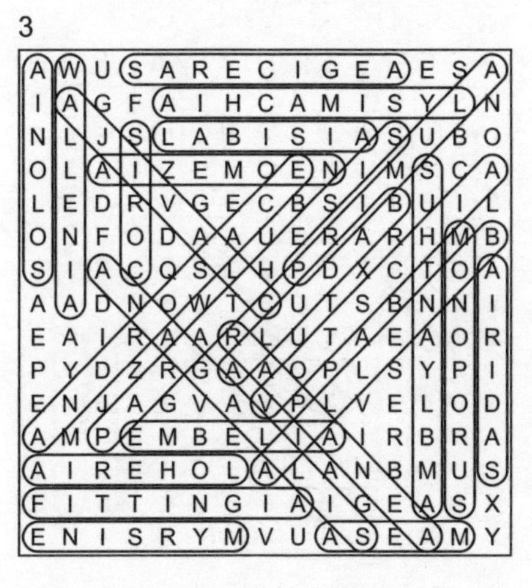

4

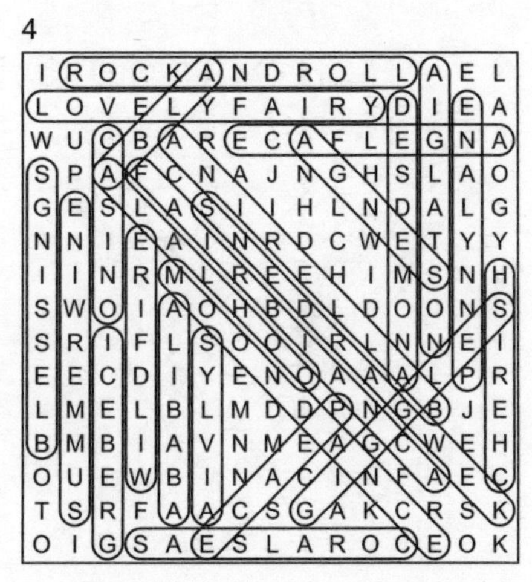

5

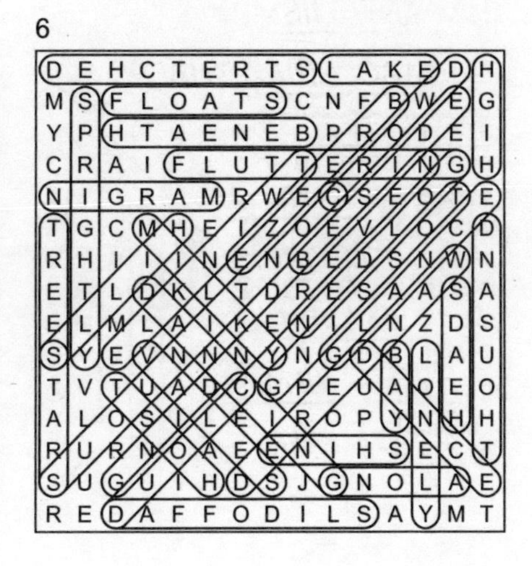

6

D E H C T E R T S L A K E D H
M S F L O A T S C N F B W E G
Y P H T A E N E B P R O D E I
C R A I F L U T T E R I N G H
N I G R A M R W E C S E O T E
T G C M H E I Z O E V L O C D
R H I I I N E N B E D S N W N
E T L D K L T D R E S A A S A
E L M L A I K E N I L N Z D S
S Y E V N N N Y N G D B L A U
T V T U A D C G P E U A O E O
A L O S I L E I R O P Y N H H
R U R N O A E E N I H S E C T
S U G U I H D S J G N O L A E
R E D A F F O D I L S A Y M T

Solutions

7

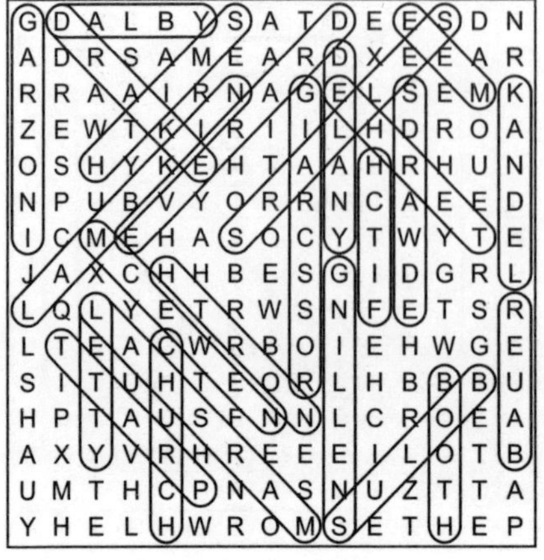

G	D	A	L	B	Y	S	A	T	D	E	E	S	D	N
A	D	R	S	A	M	E	A	R	D	X	E	E	A	R
R	R	A	A	I	R	N	A	G	E	L	S	E	M	K
Z	E	W	T	K	I	R	I	I	L	H	D	R	O	A
O	S	H	Y	K	E	H	T	A	A	H	R	H	U	N
N	P	U	B	V	Y	O	R	R	N	C	A	E	E	D
I	C	M	E	H	A	S	O	C	Y	T	W	Y	T	E
J	A	X	C	H	H	B	E	S	G	I	D	G	R	L
L	Q	L	Y	E	T	R	W	S	N	F	E	T	S	R
L	T	E	A	C	W	R	B	O	I	E	H	W	G	E
S	I	T	U	H	T	E	O	R	L	H	B	B	B	U
H	P	T	A	U	S	F	N	N	L	C	R	O	E	A
A	X	Y	V	R	H	R	E	E	E	I	L	O	T	B
U	M	T	H	C	P	N	A	S	N	U	Z	T	T	A
Y	H	E	L	H	W	R	O	M	S	E	T	H	E	P

8

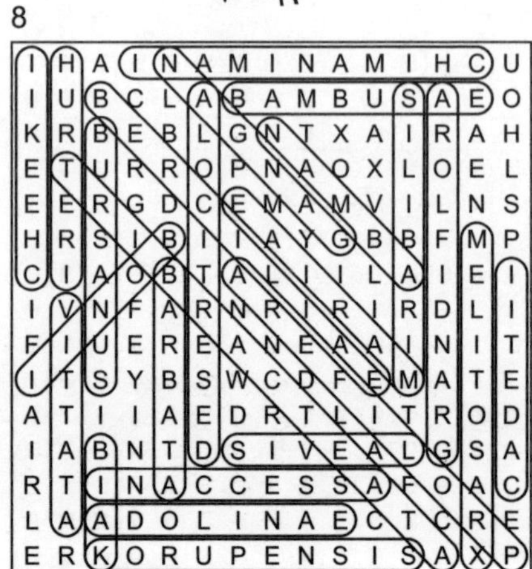

I	H	A	I	N	A	M	I	N	A	M	I	H	C	U
I	U	B	C	L	A	B	A	M	B	U	S	A	E	O
K	R	B	E	B	L	G	N	T	X	A	I	R	A	H
E	T	U	R	R	O	P	N	A	O	X	L	O	E	L
E	E	R	G	D	C	E	M	A	M	V	I	L	N	S
H	R	S	I	B	I	I	A	Y	G	B	B	F	M	P
C	I	A	O	B	T	A	L	I	I	L	A	I	E	I
I	V	N	F	A	R	N	R	I	R	I	R	D	L	I
F	I	U	E	R	E	A	N	E	A	A	I	N	I	T
I	T	S	Y	B	S	W	C	D	F	E	M	A	T	E
A	T	I	I	A	E	D	R	T	L	I	T	R	O	D
I	A	B	N	T	D	S	I	V	E	A	L	G	S	A
R	T	I	N	A	C	C	E	S	S	A	F	O	A	C
L	A	A	D	O	L	I	N	A	E	C	T	C	R	E
E	R	K	O	R	U	P	E	N	S	I	S	A	X	P

9

A	I	N	I	T	O	H	P	S	U	R	Y	P	H	S
F	A	B	R	O	S	I	U	G	N	A	S	S	U	F
S	O	R	B	A	R	O	N	I	A	T	H	B	O	A
U	P	O	P	A	C	A	S	I	B	I	R	A	E	A
T	A	I	U	G	C	I	I	Y	A	O	A	S	M	I
A	I	T	R	Y	V	A	N	L	S	O	I	E	L	O
B	G	Y	S	A	C	I	I	D	E	L	E	A	E	A
O	N	L	H	Z	E	R	I	N	Y	K	I	N	R	I
N	A	O	I	T	D	A	A	T	E	N	R	C	I	R
A	H	S	A	S	A	O	S	T	E	M	D	O	A	A
L	I	P	R	I	U	A	C	D	A	R	R	M	H	M
E	A	E	R	S	M	L	D	Y	Y	E	E	A	Z	L
M	T	R	I	O	P	A	A	A	N	N	G	R	E	U
A	E	M	C	Y	M	W	S	M	R	I	U	U	S	H
K	P	A	R	U	N	C	U	S	N	I	A	M	S	E

10

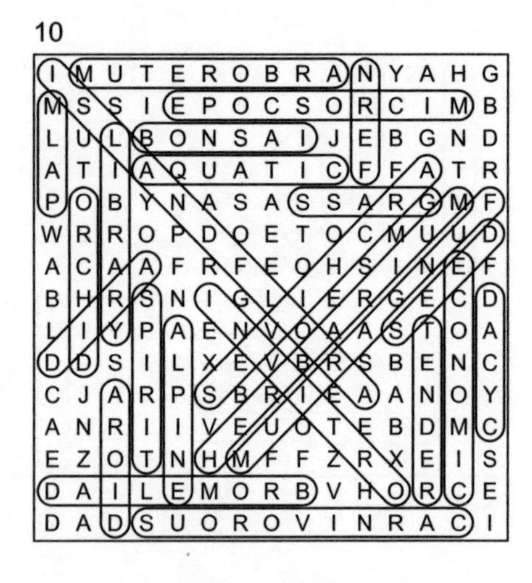

I	M	U	T	E	R	O	B	R	A	N	Y	A	H	G
M	S	S	I	E	P	O	C	S	O	R	C	I	M	B
L	U	L	B	O	N	S	A	I	J	E	B	G	N	D
A	T	I	A	Q	U	A	T	I	C	F	F	A	T	R
P	O	B	Y	N	A	S	A	S	S	A	R	G	M	F
W	R	R	O	P	D	O	E	T	O	C	M	U	U	D
A	C	A	A	F	R	F	E	O	H	S	I	N	E	F
B	H	R	S	N	I	G	L	I	E	R	G	E	C	D
L	I	Y	P	A	E	N	V	O	A	A	S	T	O	A
D	D	S	I	L	X	E	V	B	R	S	B	E	N	C
C	J	A	R	P	S	B	R	I	E	A	A	N	O	Y
A	N	R	I	I	V	E	U	O	T	E	B	D	M	C
E	Z	O	T	N	H	M	F	F	Z	R	X	E	I	S
D	A	I	L	E	M	O	R	B	V	H	O	R	C	E
D	A	D	S	U	O	R	O	V	I	N	R	A	C	I

11

A	S	S	O	L	G	O	S	S	O	R	C	E	R	O
P	P	L	A	T	Y	R	H	I	Z	A	Q	U	S	A
S	I	T	T	O	L	G	O	C	O	L	P	N	I	L
B	A	I	R	A	L	U	P	I	T	A	T	R	X	Z
A	C	U	A	I	Q	U	J	O	M	I	A	S	E	E
I	A	J	V	L	S	U	G	E	V	N	M	I	L	L
S	T	R	D	E	S	U	D	N	N	O	C	R	P	E
O	T	M	Y	O	T	I	L	E	A	S	A	A	O	N
T	L	U	V	C	N	R	G	I	A	A	L	E	M	K
O	E	P	A	P	U	A	E	A	H	K	O	L	Y	O
P	Y	I	S	N	D	P	B	A	Y	C	P	A	D	A
F	A	B	D	O	M	I	N	E	A	I	O	G	I	F
S	I	N	C	Y	C	Y	L	O	P	D	G	C	D	C
T	R	O	P	I	D	I	A	G	A	R	O	S	S	F
S	U	T	S	A	L	B	I	P	E	V	N	P	Q	A

12

B	O	C	A	R	P	H	O	C	H	A	E	T	E	F
A	R	A	P	O	T	O	S	P	E	R	M	U	M	U
G	E	I	A	M	B	M	F	U	N	G	A	R	N	F
S	H	X	D	M	Z	R	Z	A	E	S	S	E	J	A
P	C	Y	A	X	U	H	E	U	H	S	E	A	P	A
H	I	Z	E	M	L	I	M	B	A	R	D	A	A	I
I	R	Y	D	V	O	U	B	N	M	P	E	L	R	L
L	T	Z	T	Z	H	C	T	O	E	A	I	S	A	U
A	I	V	E	T	S	O	O	T	R	H	A	I	G	E
C	P	A	S	E	S	H	A	R	P	T	L	B	Y	R
T	E	E	F	I	G	L	D	O	E	U	E	E	N	V
I	D	N	A	Z	A	R	C	A	L	T	I	P	O	E
S	M	U	S	C	H	L	E	R	I	A	E	A	X	H
U	S	I	T	C	A	N	E	A	H	C	O	H	Y	C
E	N	E	O	J	E	F	F	R	E	Y	A	D	S	X

Solutions

13

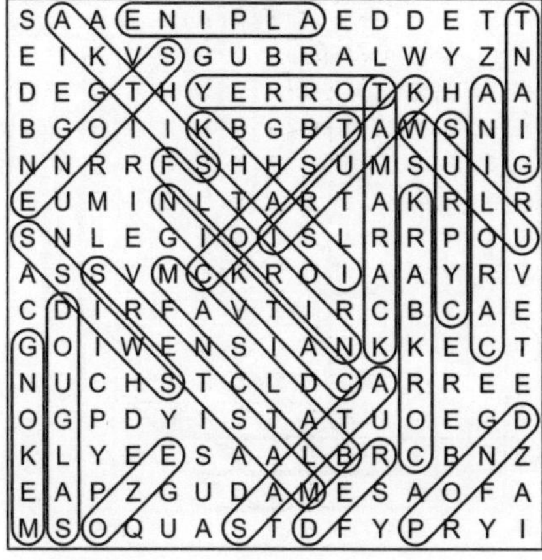

14

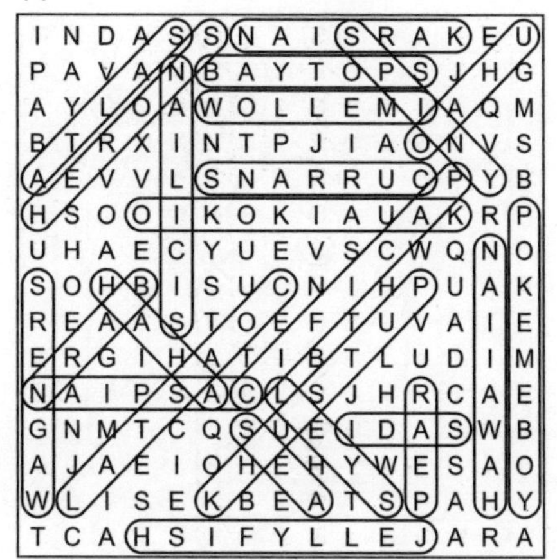

15

16

17

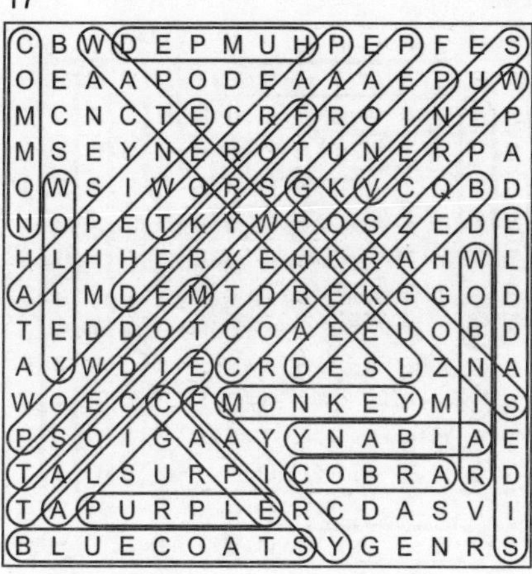

18

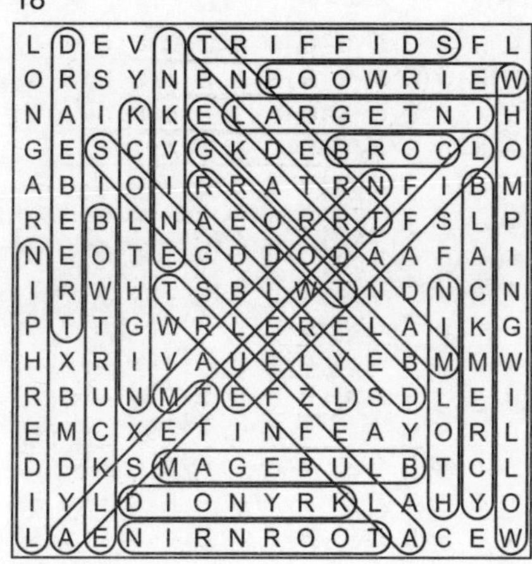

Solutions

19

N O R A P A T U L B X H L S O
O N E S I O T A Q Z V E F Z F
A J N Q B S A I N A C I L Q T
I C Y N O M E T R A K O K I A
C E S S E H T N A R Y H C A I
R B P N A I G I A S O H Y I S
Y Y O O E I A U I M P Z Z R O
M T R P C E R C E R O I I A R
A T O S J I G E A T N P D E H
C N B I D A L D T L T X M S C
R E O A S Z O E A U Y A Q A O
U R L D T S Q F M E O P R C C
D I U I I V I O L A P P H D Q
I A S A D I A N T U M O X A A
A O R B E X I L U M Z L H G T

20

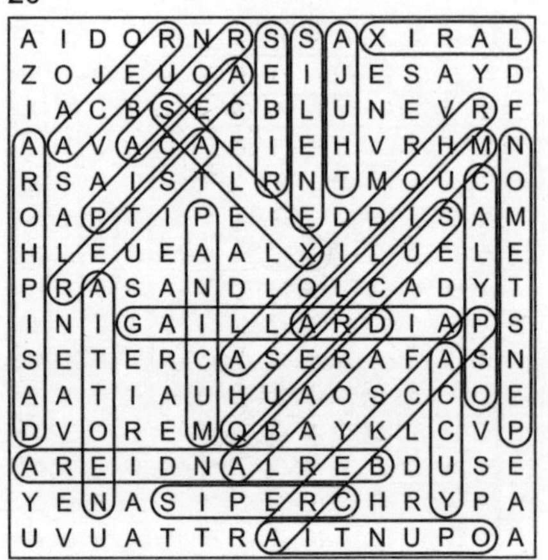

21

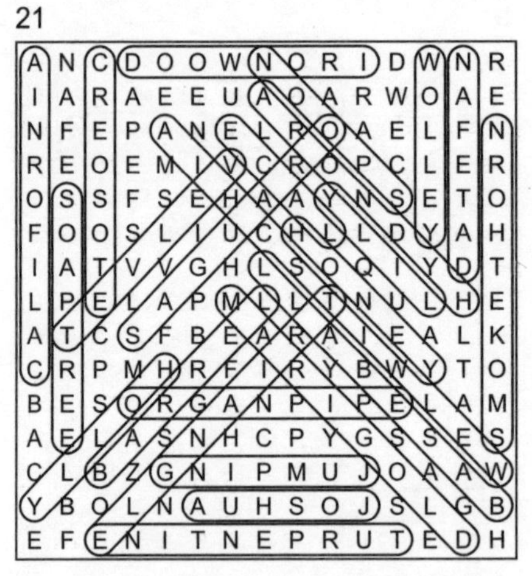

22

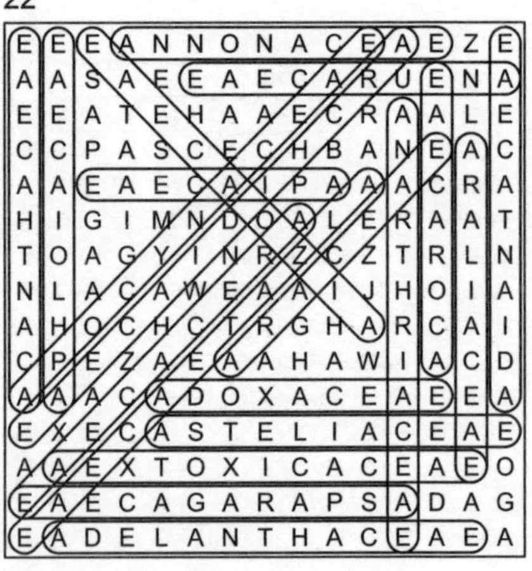

23

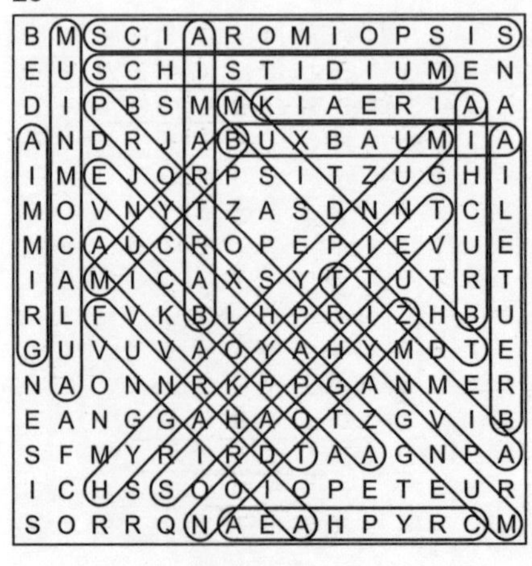

24

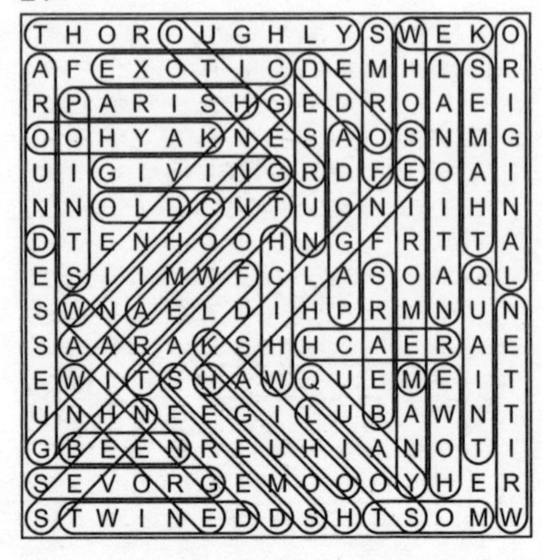

Solutions

25

L T E S A T E U G N E B A D R
E A S T E R A D T E T O E U A
O N V A D A N A C S R Y S E Y
P O T P O Q H R Y A A W O O D
A G H S N C E E N R E T S E W
R A B U O W L G N I S S G O N
D T Z G M L E E H A N S O N S
R R D I E B D N C G D F K O E
E A E K L L O E I L R E G I I
D M S G O L A L G P L A D P U
P L T G I C H Y D L L Y Y D R
S Y B S E T A C O T A A C S I
H E N R Y S A G E R S C A G H
W A S H I N G T O N P S Y E S
V A R E S S N A I R E B I S A

26

H S E S E N A P A J G R E A Y
A S U W A E R B C N E V E S Y
Y H I G R A I N I G R I V O N
N A V C A R A R E T N I W Z A
O G J A D R E M Q L H C G L C
R B U T O W T V P H O D M C I
T A K A O R U B I M P I Y P R
H R P L W C H Y M R E A D A E
E K F P W S A O F L C B R C M
R V P A O B N E N M A O A I A
N F F N R E T S A E N L H F O
A L C O R N E L I A N O T I J
I M A K A T S U R A N E H C L
T A G D E Y D R A B M O L F S
S E R A Y G N I K A U Q U E T

27

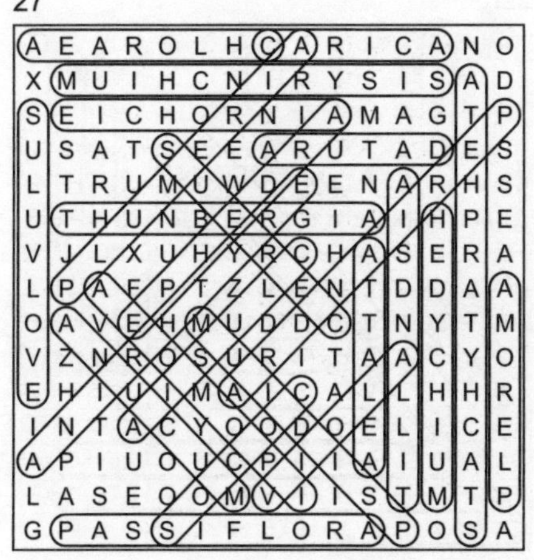

28

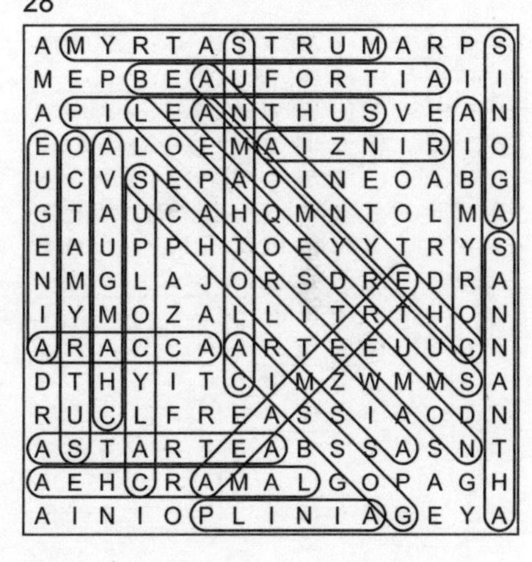

29

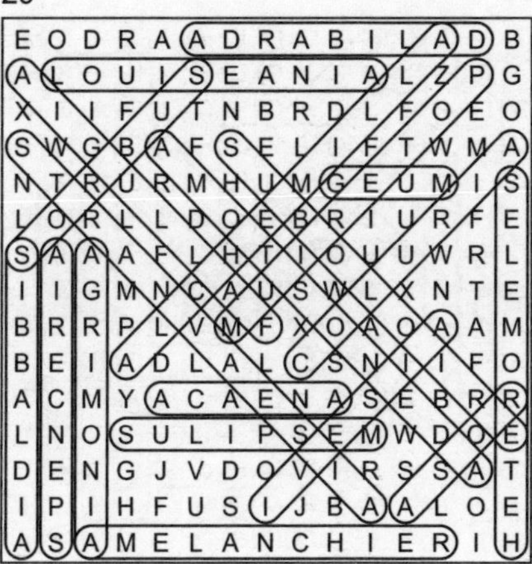

30

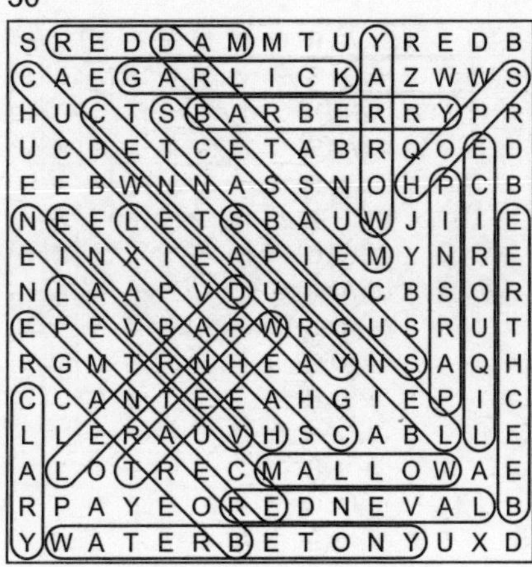

Solutions

31

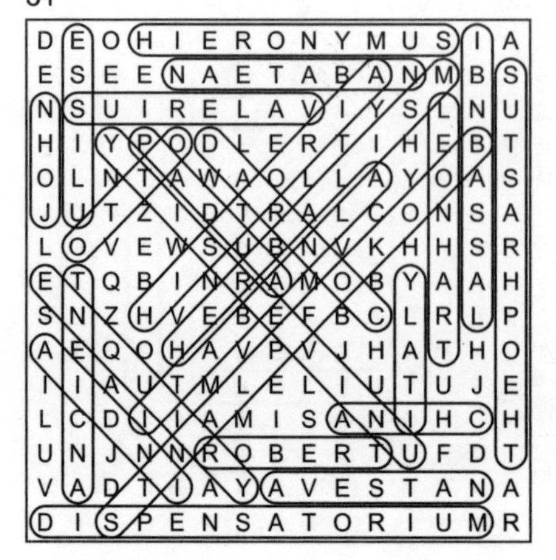

32

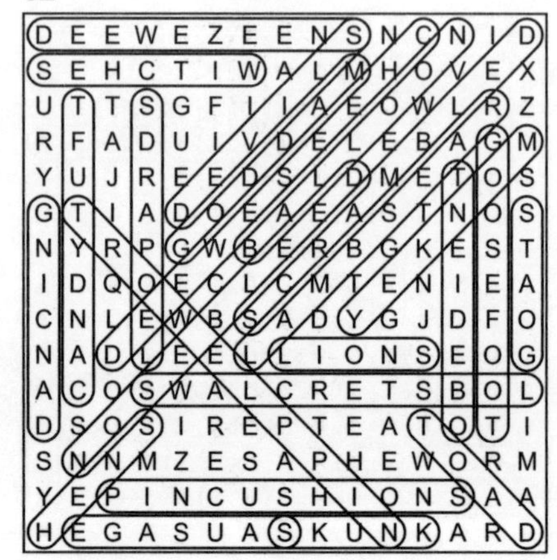

33

34

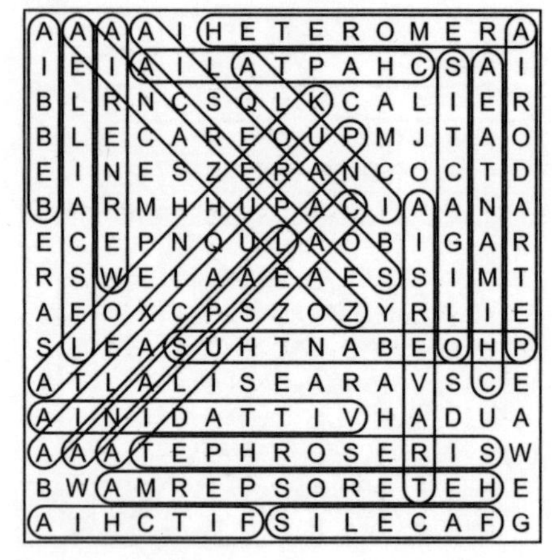

35

36

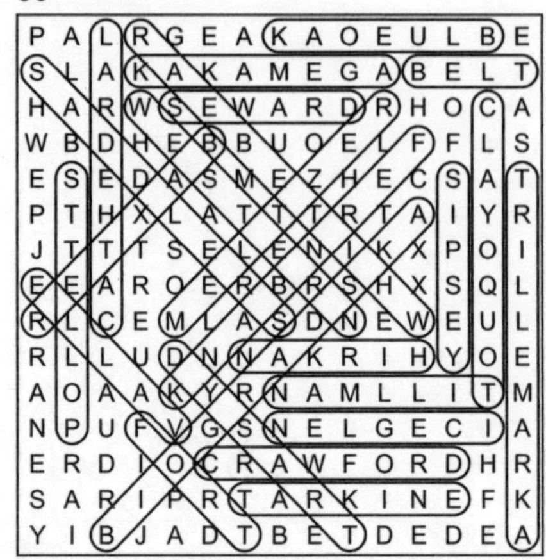

Solutions

37

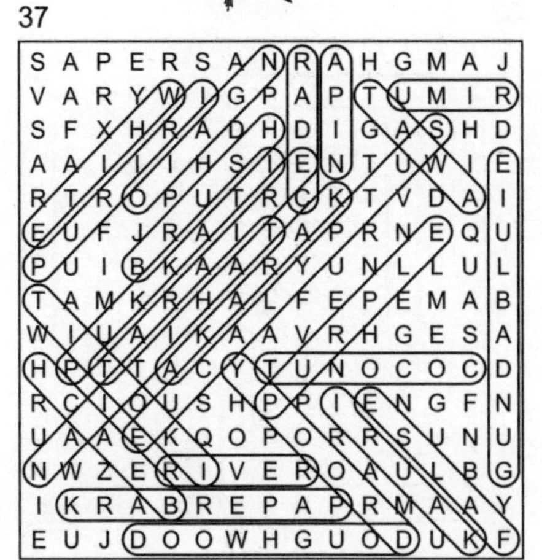

38

39

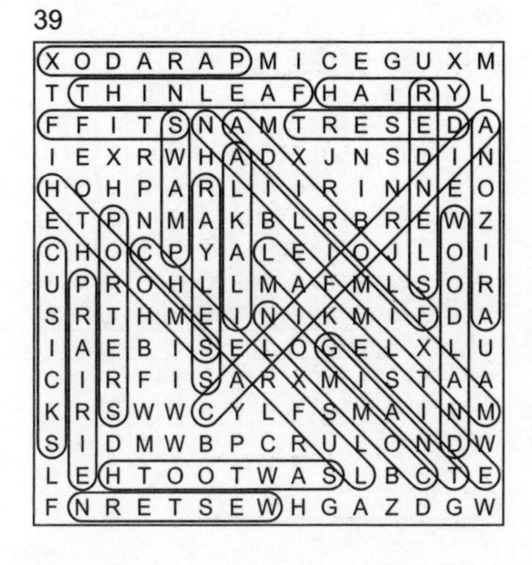

40

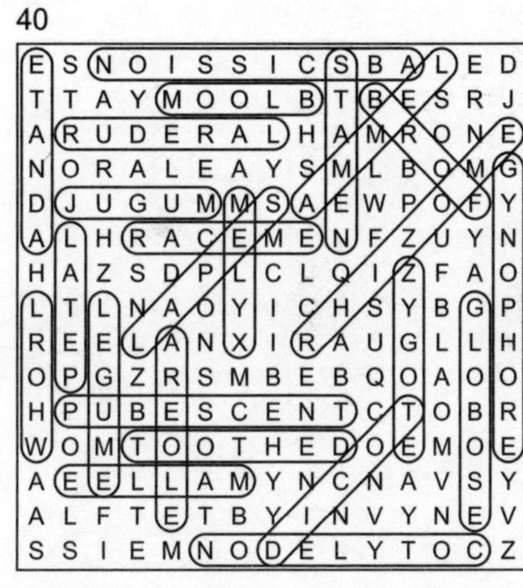

41

42

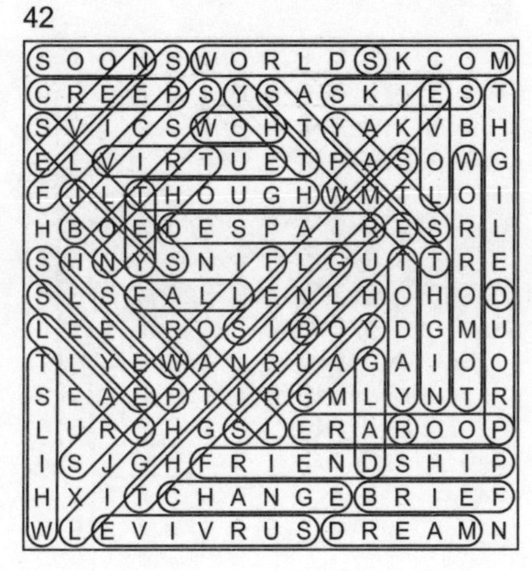

Solutions

43

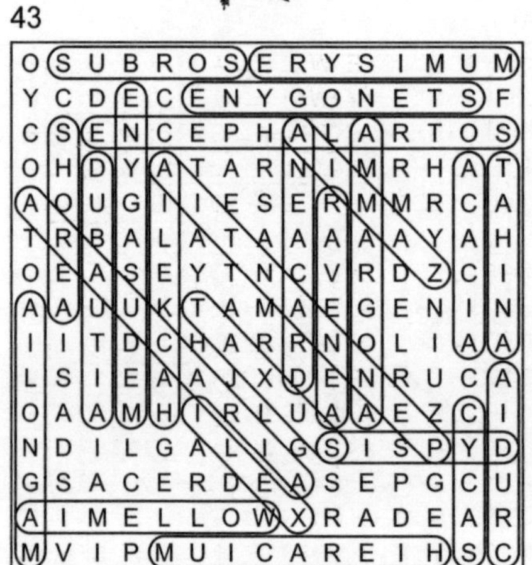

44

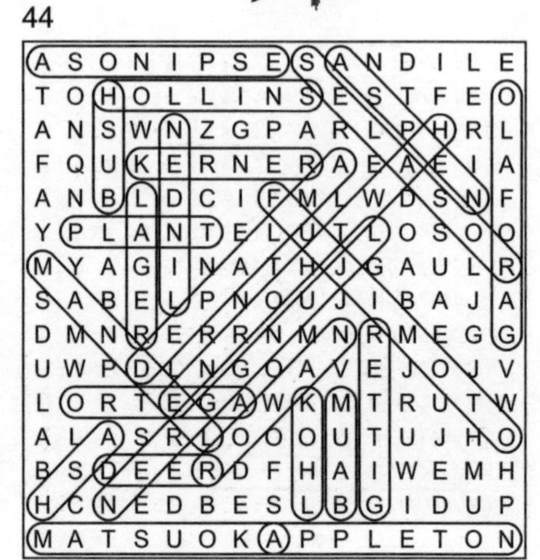

45

C S U C O R C A L Y B T E P P
L I N O G E L I U R Y U E D A
A I T F I G L L O R A L O T M
R T G T E Y Z O T A C I N S A
G F I R A Z K T E R W P U R R
E A N V E L S U U I Y T N O I
T O G A Y E S S L Y P S O L G
N Y Y N F S N L A Y U X I E O
I H V W E D O W L R T U L A L
D B N R N W A A O E W I E N D
I R P R S R C H A O L N D D E
H Y E G A U F R L A D A N E C
C F O F E I O O C I R O A R A
R S N E T S E S U Q A A D P S
O P Y H E U N S D E S E R T T

46

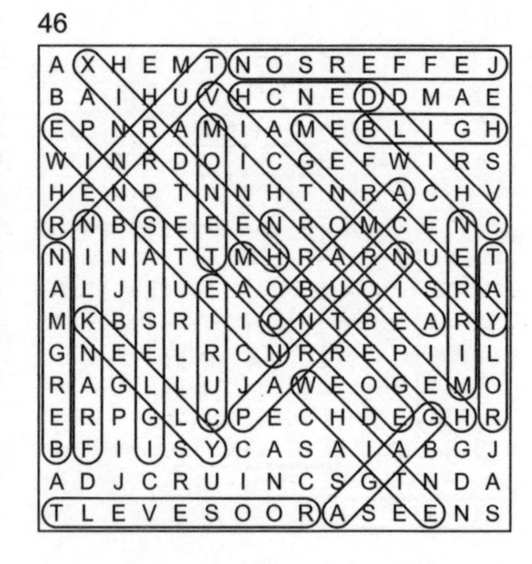

47

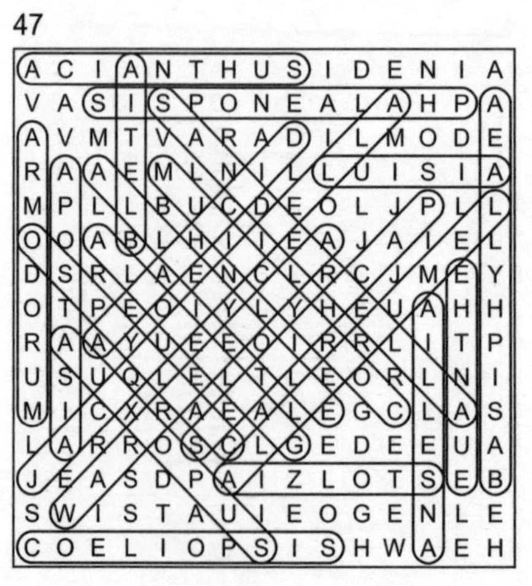

48

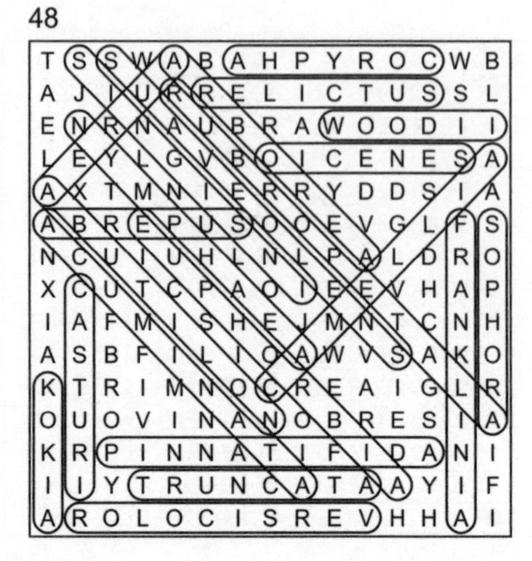

Solutions

49

A I N W T H E L Y P O D I U M
A O N V E S U N A S Y H T A A
H M W P E R A Y C N I O C E R
M B U F S F D A D A V E N L E
A U E I F U M E S A O P M G H
A E I R D B H A R I Y G I N T
L I N D O I R T H M R A A I N
I J N P O E P F N C A E D R A
H V U I I H T E A A R N B P L
P S F R R D T U L R C O N I E
O H O I A U D H O T S L U I T
I M W H C L A S C D X E A G A
L S O R Y U L R F O S N T H M
E A A I H C I E R D L E H I C
H A I K C E R E V I H C S F A

50

51

S M L N E M O D G E D Y S A D
Y O A G H I A V W H E C D S O
E D A N I H A T H A V I C C U
S A O T N H H C N E R F A E G
A A R A L S D S U R V F R N U
C E H S T O G N A U E S O S M
E L T T O B A T L G T S L I W
S U V W F I S E A O G T I O O
H G X H S E T B B J N T N N O
I O W R U T B C D V C E E B D
B G A L E A E N E S E L S T S
S K B I C I T H R I W T A A D
N O R E W A X E N N A R L Y V
O A H G A P S A M A K A N X S
P R I B B Y C G M I D B Y E M

52

53

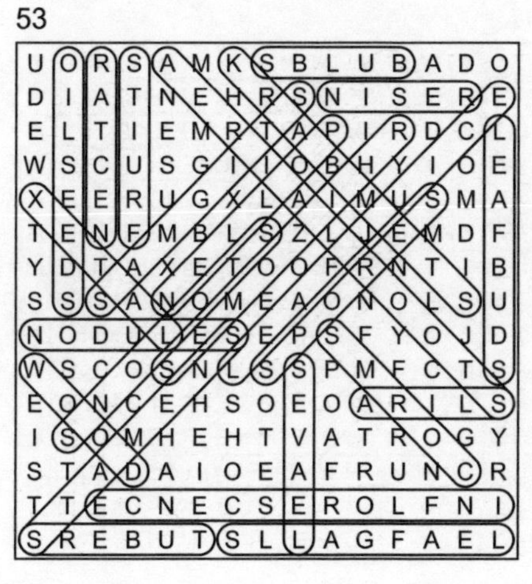

54

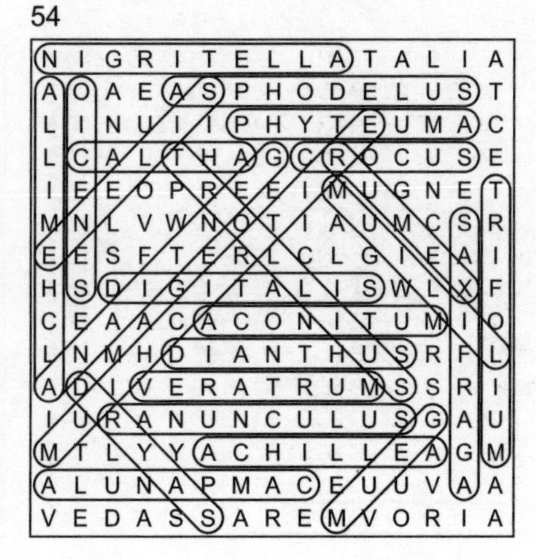

Solutions

55

S	O	G	N	F	R	A	H	Z	D	N	A	R	T	S
B	K	E	E	R	G	D	E	V	A	E	L	E	N	O
T	N	R	S	E	A	P	I	R	M	A	E	V	W	P
J	A	O	P	N	M	I	D	L	A	N	D	I	B	I
M	E	M	E	C	M	L	E	H	C	Y	W	L	M	F
D	N	A	I	H	F	K	W	C	H	H	A	O	D	R
L	A	C	T	A	C	E	W	Y	U	C	X	L	U	F
R	R	Y	L	O	N	D	E	L	K	C	E	P	S	U
O	R	S	L	V	A	D	C	S	L	I	D	V	K	Y
W	E	D	A	F	I	N	I	J	F	G	P	C	A	N
D	T	J	S	F	L	A	O	T	R	L	A	W	S	E
L	I	M	A	R	I	T	I	M	E	R	R	X	R	P
O	D	F	B	G	C	E	Y	P	C	O	R	W	L	S
B	E	V	E	B	I	R	E	U	N	S	F	T	N	A
M	M	W	B	D	S	C	W	X	E	T	I	V	I	R

56

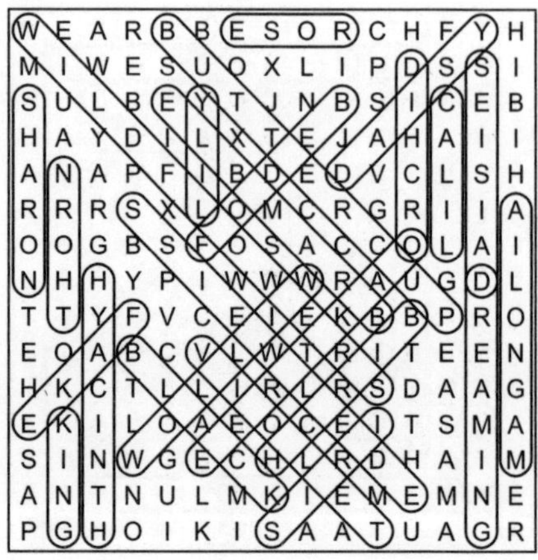

57

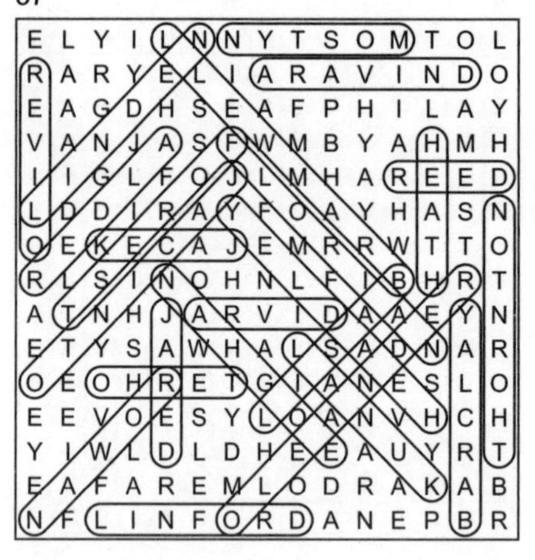

58

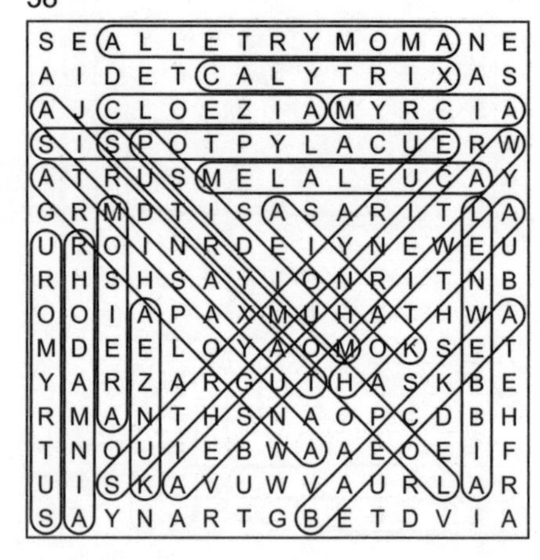

59

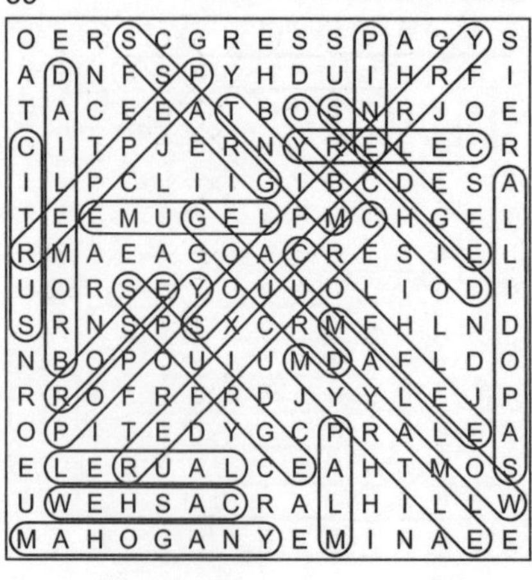

60

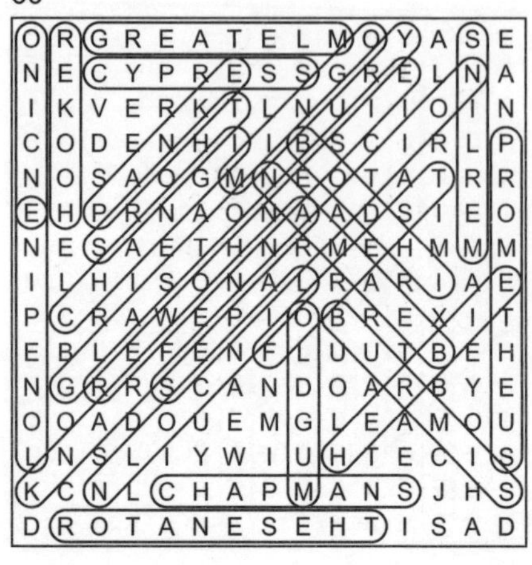

Solutions

61

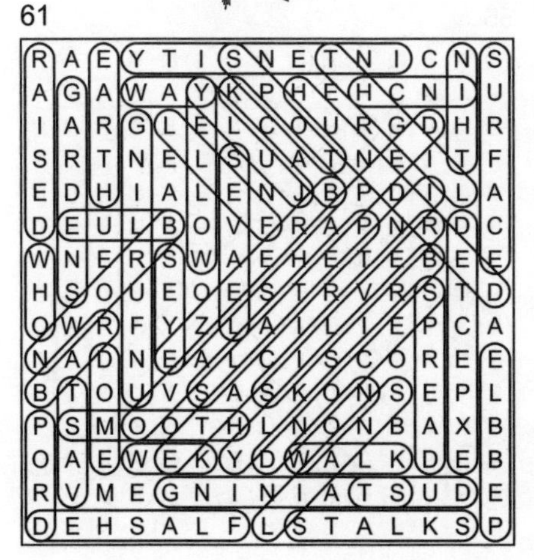

62

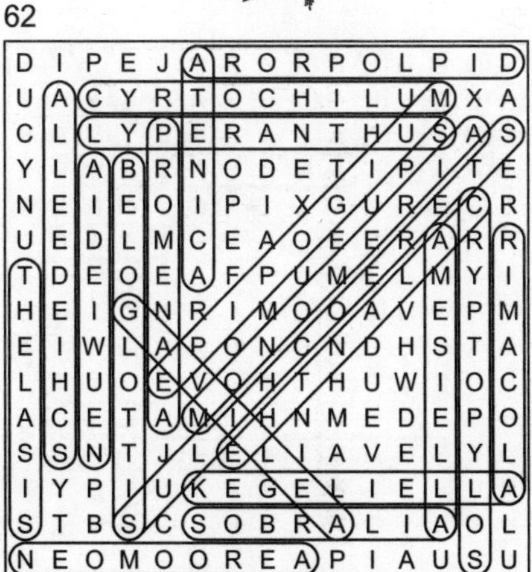

63

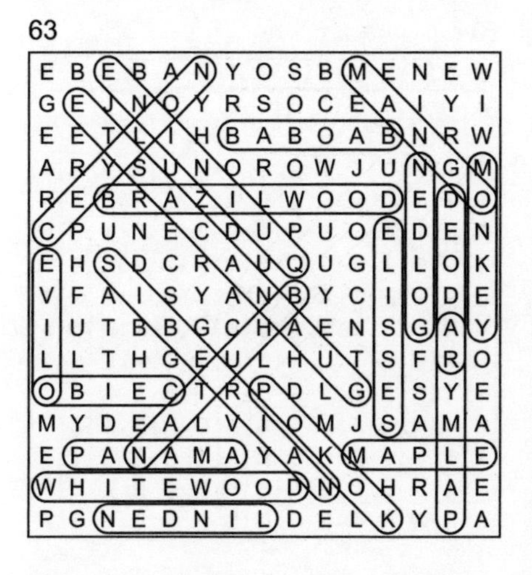

64

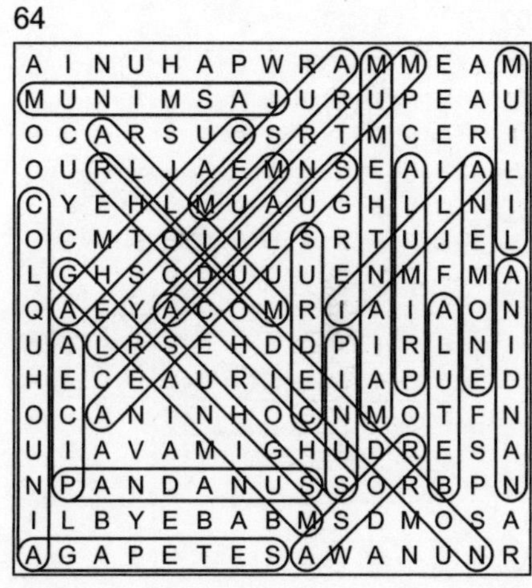

65

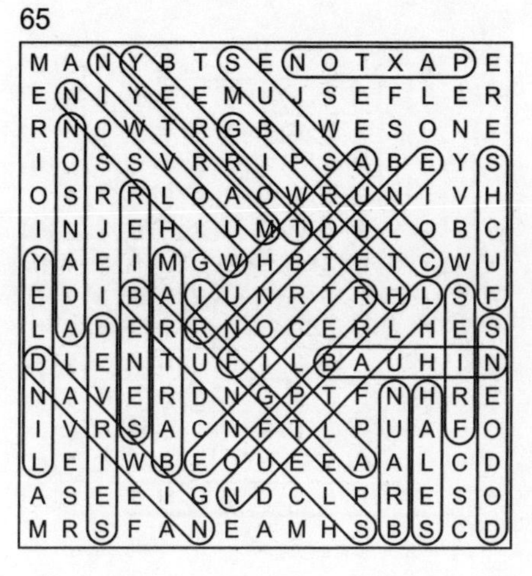

66

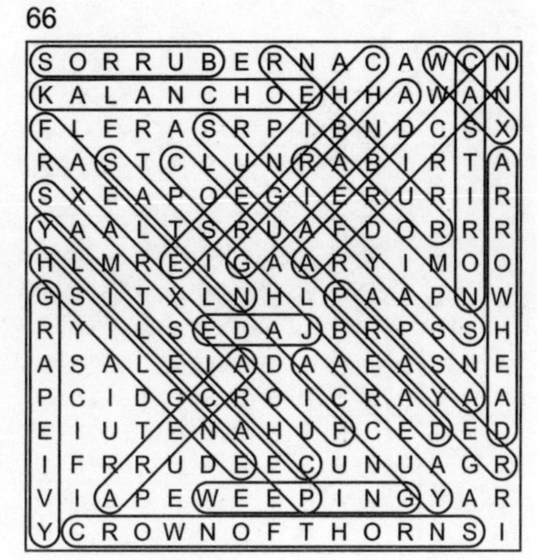

Solutions

67

68

69

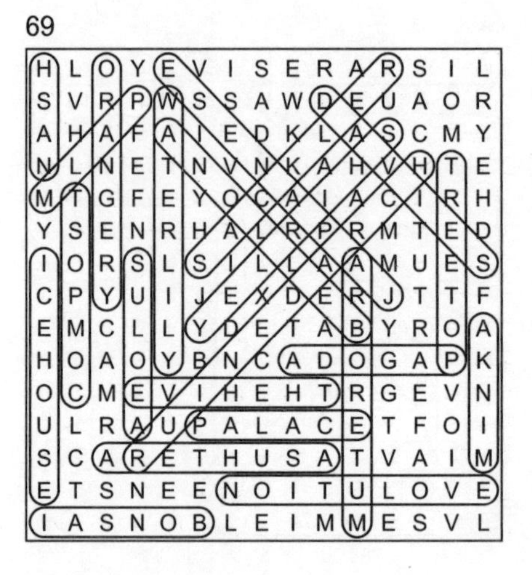

70

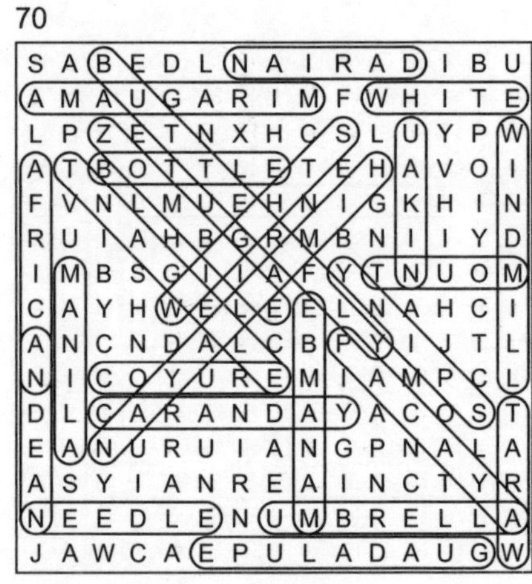

71

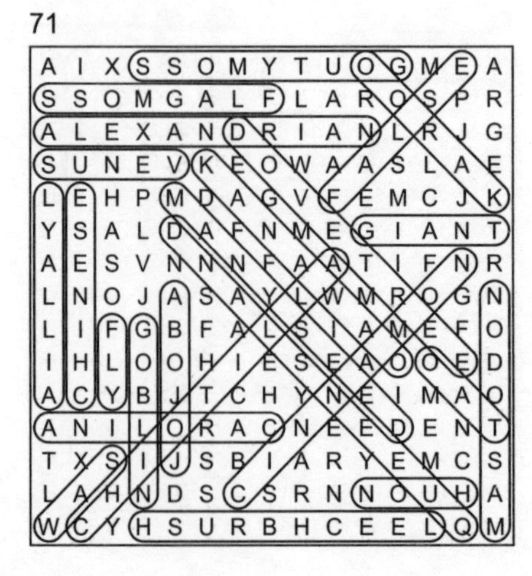

72

Solutions

73

B B I S M A R C K N L A D Y Y
M A J E S T I C O S T L W U L
H Y M A C A R T H U R I A T L
E L V E Y A R E N Y I P R U E
C V O L R E R L A E X S F N J
A I N U H I E O T N K T F O D
R Y L T L T A A L V E I A C R
O S A L E U O T C I C C N O Y
H A H B A C H R I D N K N C A
C O B S I T T I E L V A W H I
O S O T T R E H W G O S A G O
H U T P I I W M X A N S S E H
C E R A E B Y D D E T I D S E
P S U G A R A L F O T A F R D
X F O R M O S A I R A Z A M A

74

V E E B A Y L E A F L V E R A
O N A G E R O W C G I Y H B S
U S H S A V N H O R V A U T E
E O E H U R A N I B R X J C R
L R H E B M O Y S N E O H R O
T R Y L O C L B G C H I V E S
T E U M A C D I O N C R L D S
E L I F I O H R S O H L U N O
N L E L Y P I W R A I I R E N
E I R N B A O Y B D B F G V I
S A T M N R O E C A R A W A Y
G U I D T E M Y H T S P Y L V
L N E T N I F B U R D O C K A
T R N E D N Y E L S R A P A E
U H O L S S A R G N O M E L O

75

A I T N O M E R F Y E A M M Y
A I S H C U F N B E I I E X R
A I R W S V P B H L G S V V R
C E G V U U U P L P O B I Y E
A S L N Y R R E B R A B R O B
R S D A H B M B K A U D G V W
A A A S Z A N C E R E A I D O
G G O P C A O A N L S I N O N
P E V V A R R U C V T Z I G S
O B I C V I M A Y I Y T A H E
S R C Y P E B H E G X U O O W
S U B S H Y D R A N G E A B E
Y S M O K E T R E E Y D M B S
H H W U X K R A B E N I N L R
F R I N G E T R E E C W I E O

76

T F V F R O L R E D N E V A L
U R T R R I F I R M R U W F W
L D I C T Y E V F E V I L O G
P E H F O R R E O E T O S N X
A I A F F A N O E L W P E X M
D E E F G I Y R E E S K E A A
W O N S M X D O R E O D R C G
P H W S M D M S E R A I T C N
W S A L U D W E B H G W Y A O
I J E D W R A S L O F U R C L
L A Y N A V E I L B E B U T I
L H U S I I A D S F H O N U A
O V H Y N P S O N I I P A S S
W B O R E H R Y U U E R O C B
S M S Y R A M E S O R S B E N

77

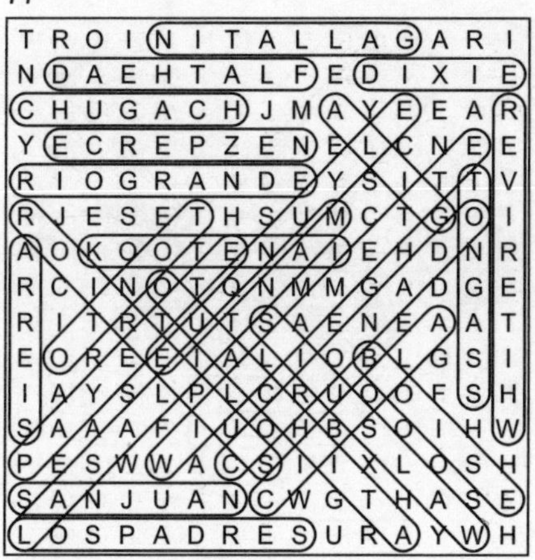

T R O I N I T A L L A G A R I
N D A E H T A L F E D I X I E
C H U G A C H J M A Y E E A R
Y E C R E P Z E N E L C N E E
R I O G R A N D E Y S I T T V
R J E S E T H S U M C T G O I
A O K O O T E N A I E H D N R
R C I N O T Q N M M G A D G E
R I T R T U T S A E N E A A T
E O R E E I A L I O B L G S I
I A Y S L P L C R U O O F S H
S A A A F I U O H B S O I H W
P E S W W A C S I I X L O S H
S A N J U A N C W G T H A S E
L O S P A D R E S U R A Y W H

78

T N E T N O C S I D H T O W N
D O W D N F R U N S E T D Y S
W M G I I A E L O T S E R C E
O H A W I D F L O W E R D A V
S G A R D E N B O W E R R N E
A L B V O N C E E D E O T D I
L T A W E M G B L A O O I C H
R T N O G N F I D P W W A L T
A D E N I O G G E E S S X L H
I E D D I H L O R F T Y I A G
S S N E T G P D A E C T O C U
E I E S I L H B E R W T W J O
B R R R E R L T O N A E A O N
L E O U D E C W X L N R A C E
Y S W C E H N C L T Y P R A F

Solutions

79

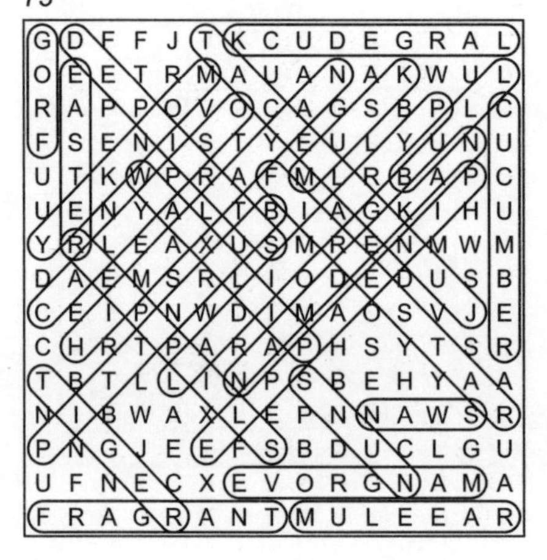

80

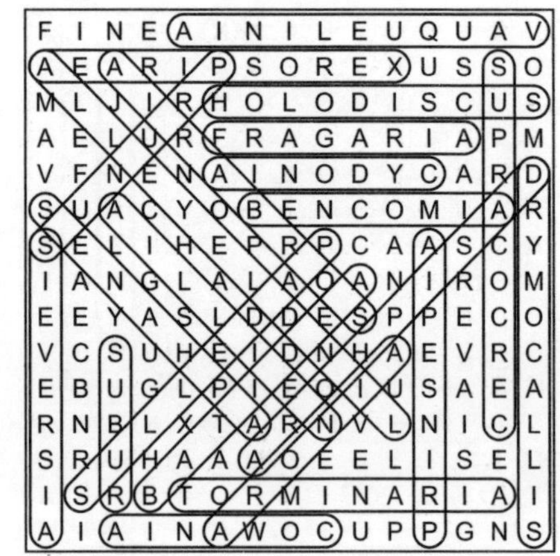

81

82

83

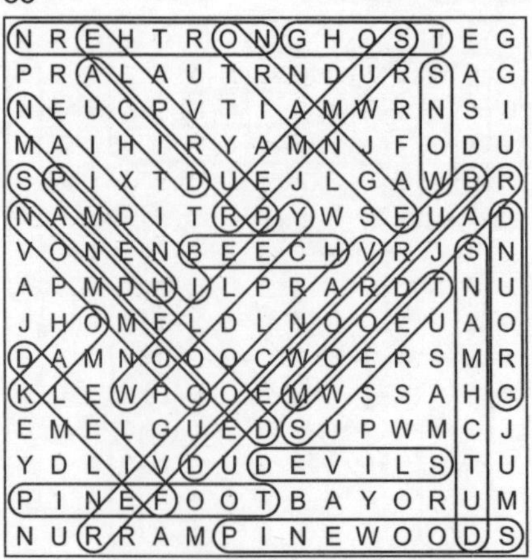

84

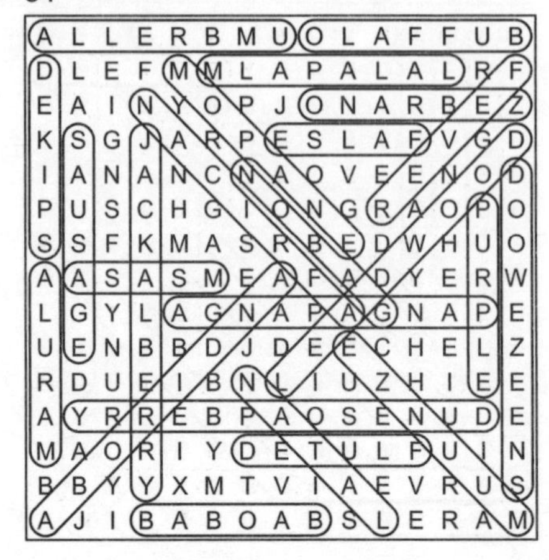

Solutions

85

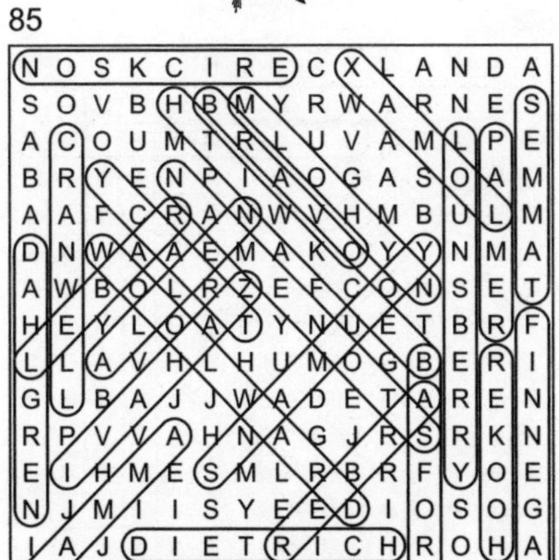

86

87

L R D L E I H S T F O S V A B
I L I L O L Y V A C R A B E D
I B D A I C J N R O H G A T S
H R N N H I H K F C H A I N R
E A C L O S T R I C H O E H A
P C W A K M U A I M O T O C B
A K K Y A T M N U S B A J E B
C E L O N S Y O E T T E L E I
K N I R G P S H C V U M R B T
C R D N A N X T N C F M A L S
O E E O R G I O R H M R N S Y
R H E T O B T G A A O M D B A
N T R T O S P R N U H U R A S
I O F U O I D G G A W V S N E
L M E B T E T H I T H R G E P

88

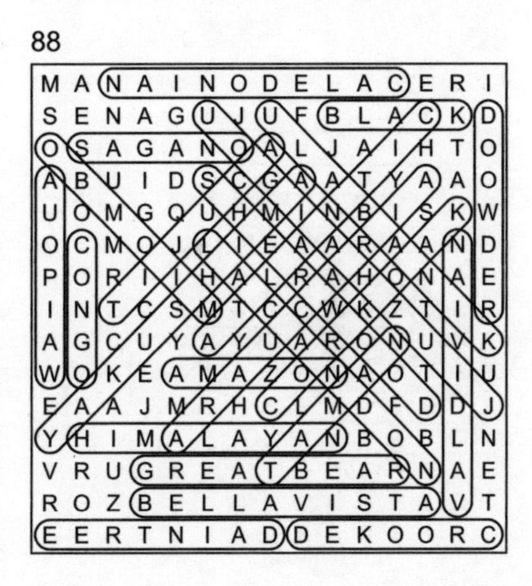

89

E A B A F Y N I L A P E M J O
S I S I D I P H Y S C I U M L
I S I R I T A R E I A A I A T
P E P E B A R B U L A I D C S
O T E K Y S E J L A C L I P P
R S L O B C B E I N V G H Y L
T O O O F R B R Y I P A C S A
Y C C H Y M O R I T G V R E G
L J U M I L L F I N D O A L I
B U E L Y I N L U O W R M I O
M L L A G R I M I F Y A L G M
A R T N V U E R T H U G R E N
N O I N M O L A C D R E U R I
M U I R T I M O C S Y H P I U
P H Y S C O M I T R E L L A M

90

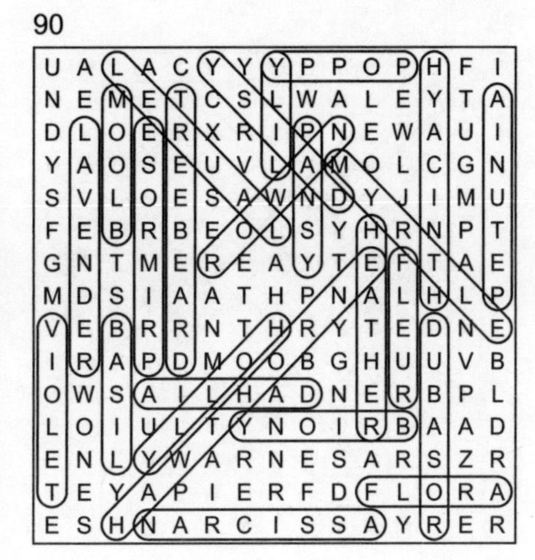

Solutions

91

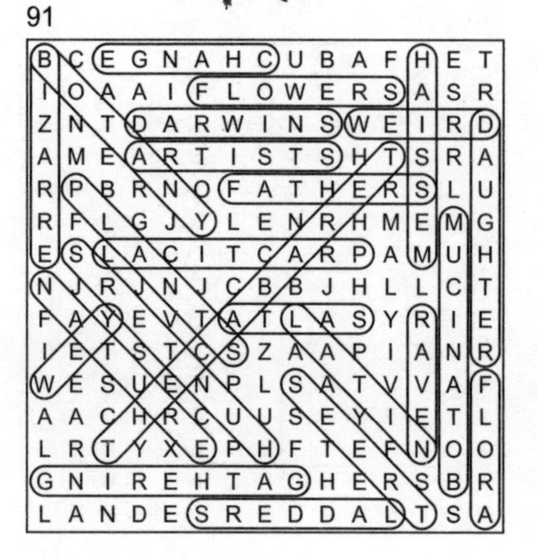

92

93

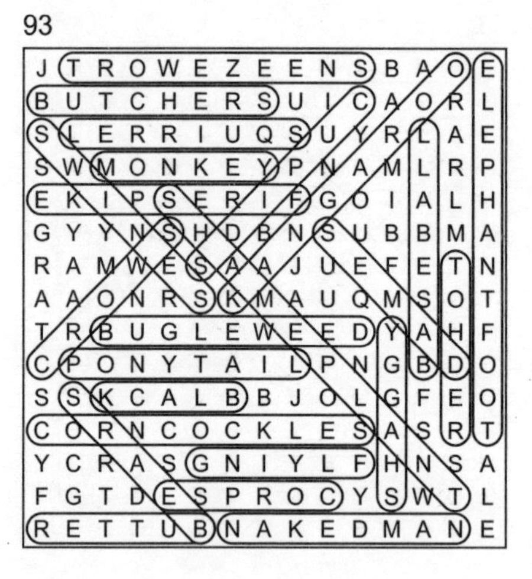

94

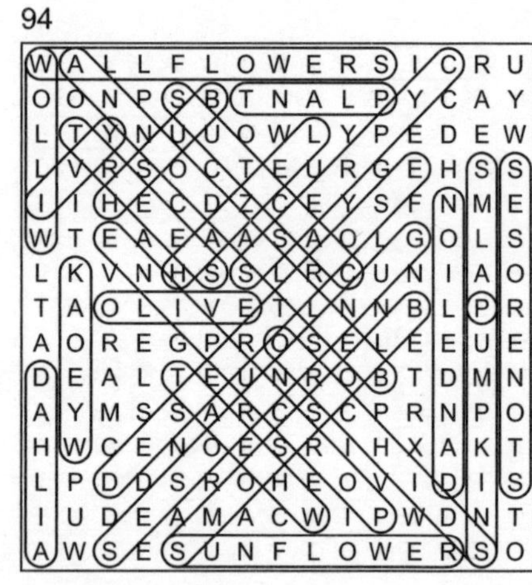

95

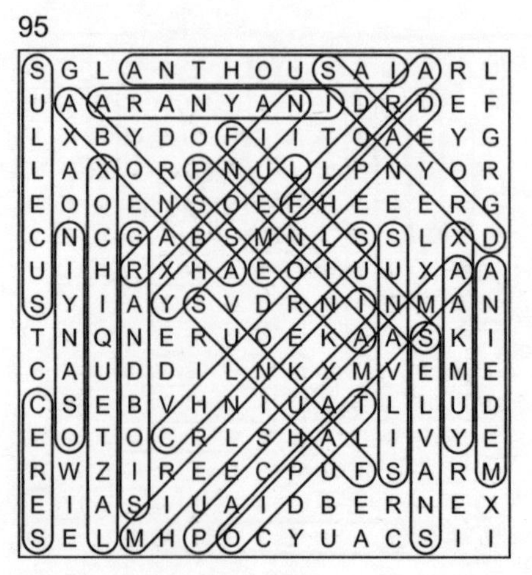

96

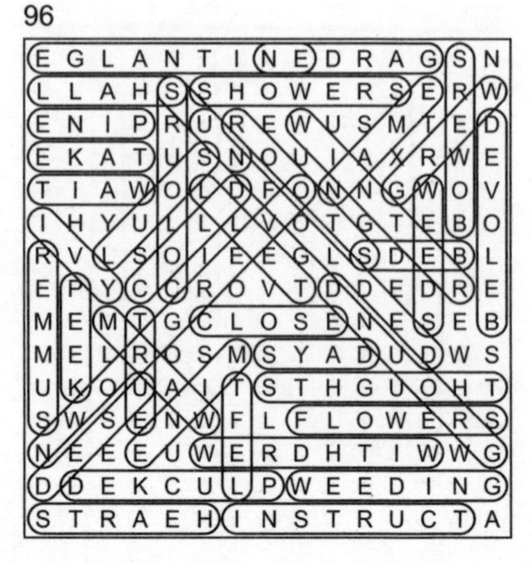

Solutions

97

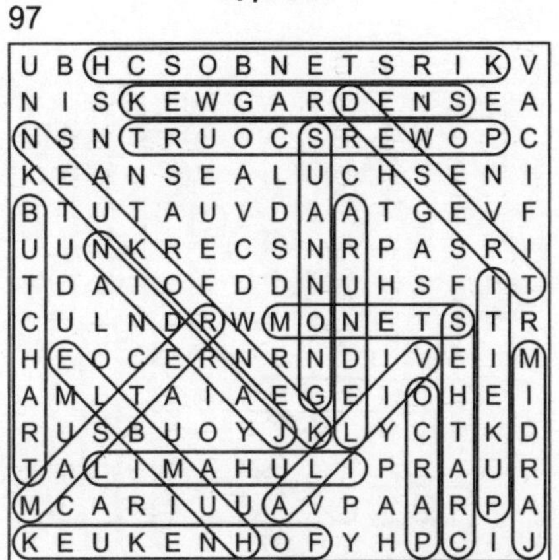

98

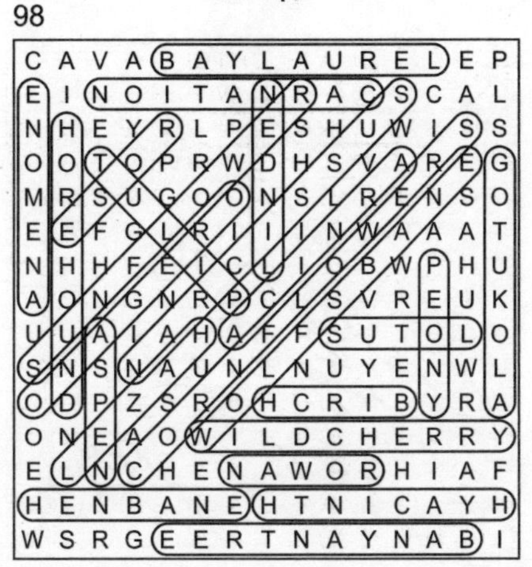

99

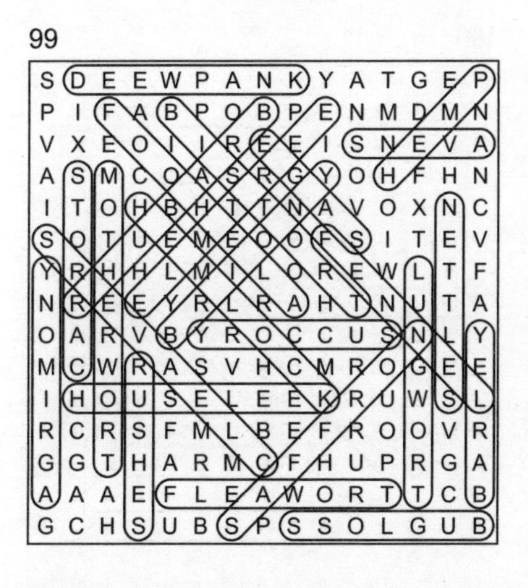

100

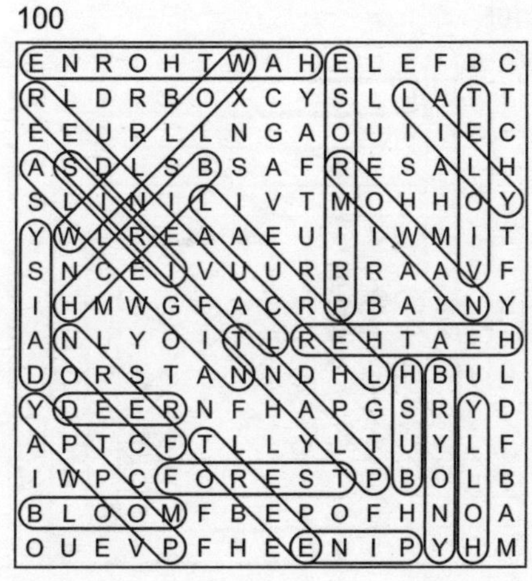

101

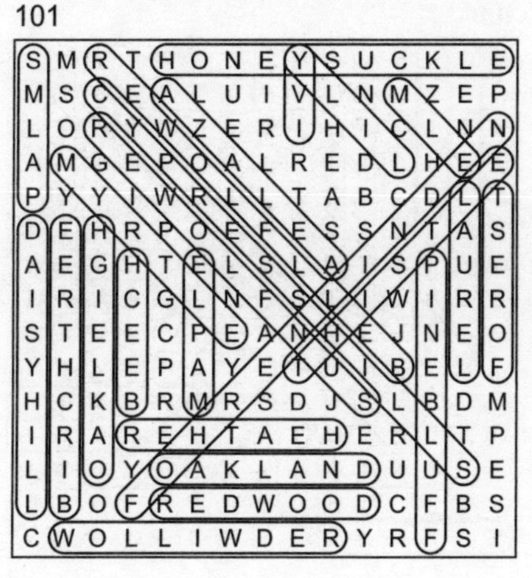

102

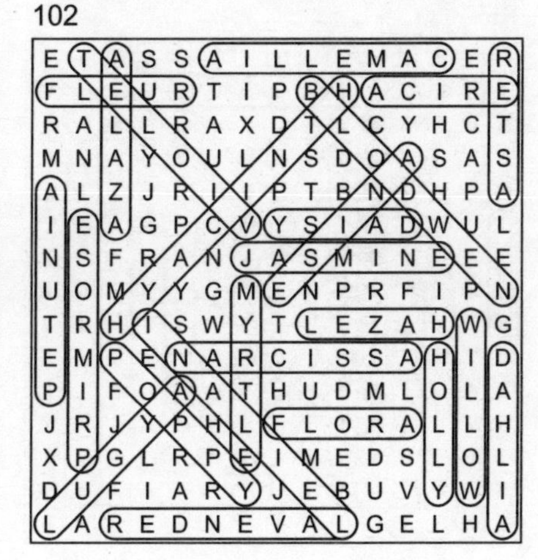

Solutions

103

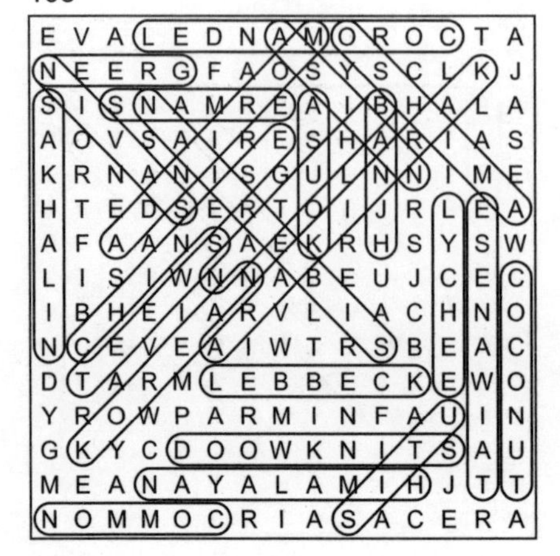

104

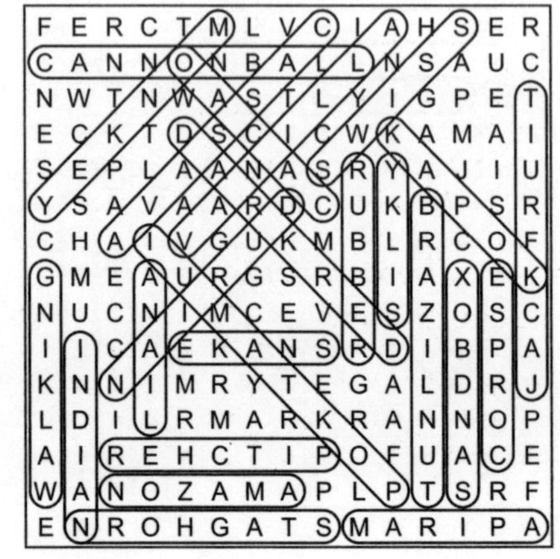

105

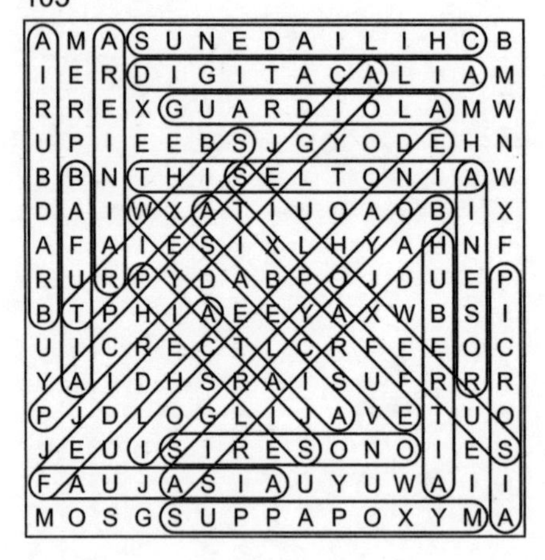

106

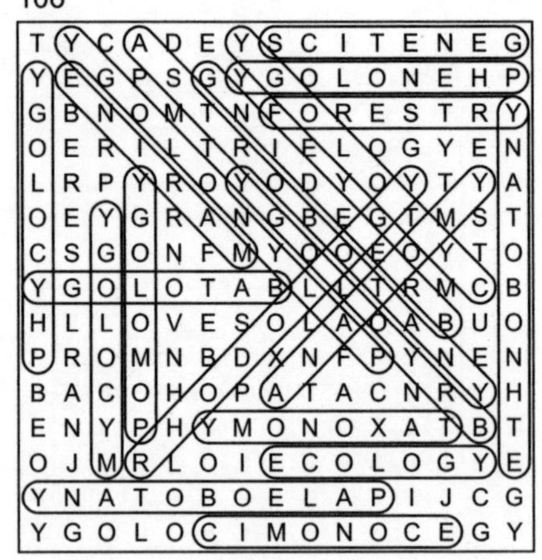

107

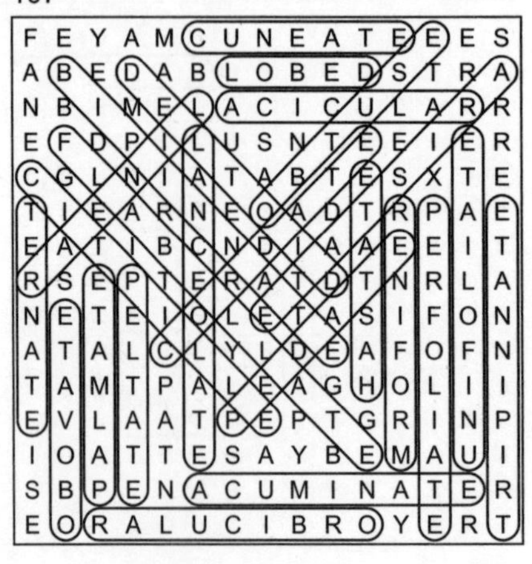

108

Solutions

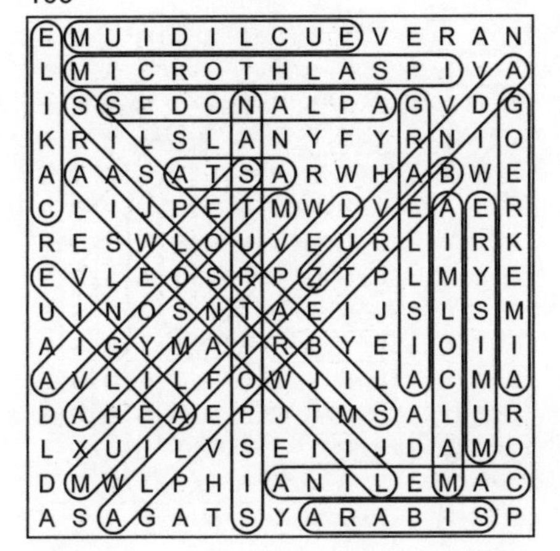

110

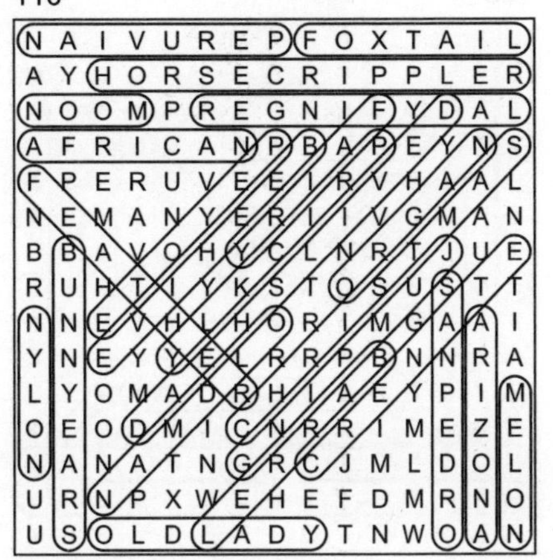

111

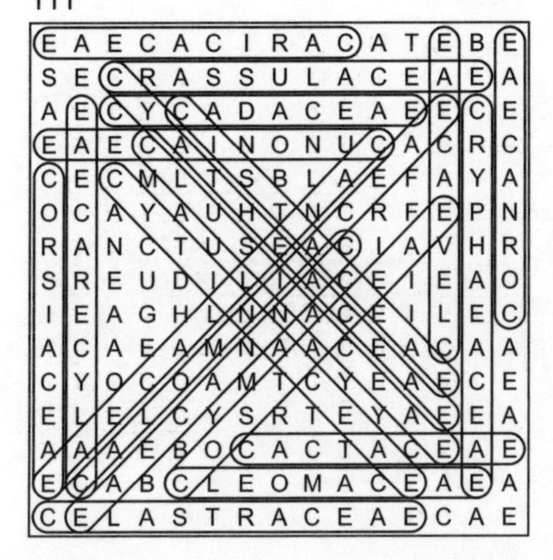

112

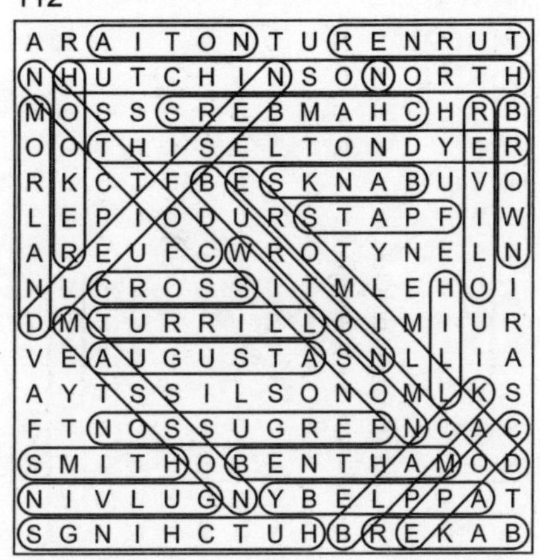

113

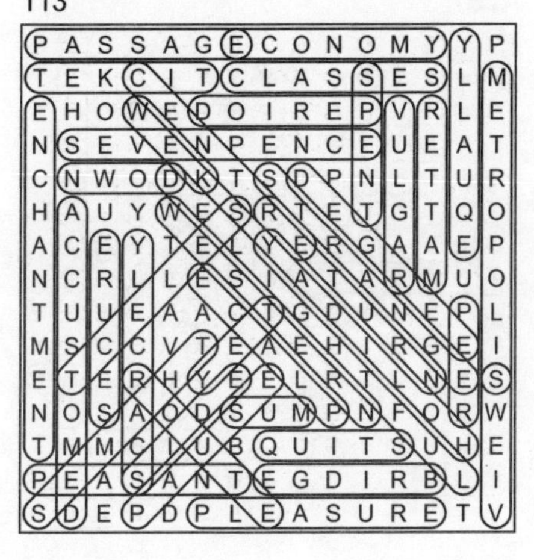

114

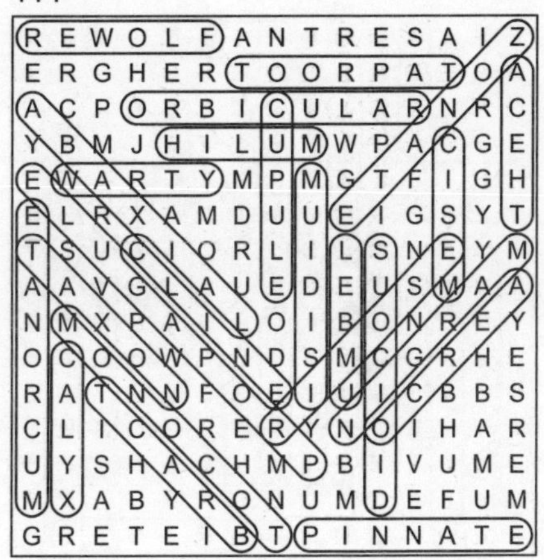

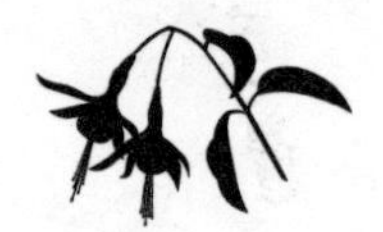

Solutions

115

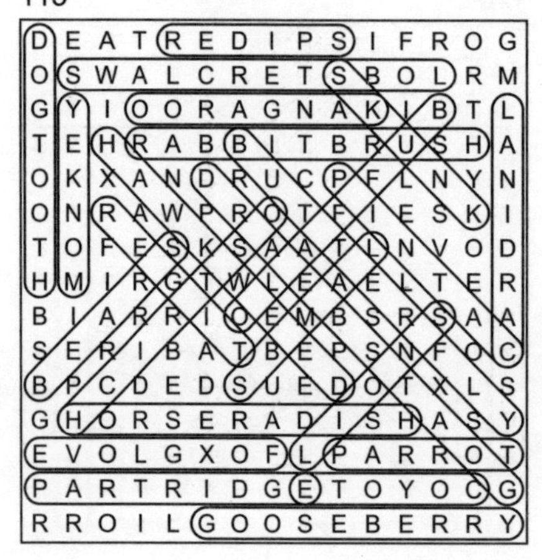

116

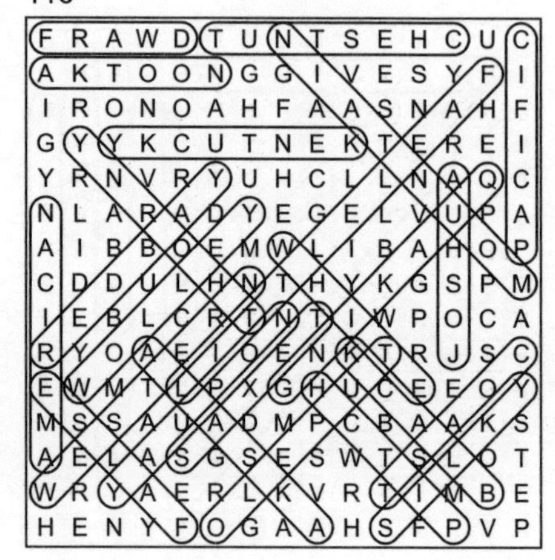

117

118

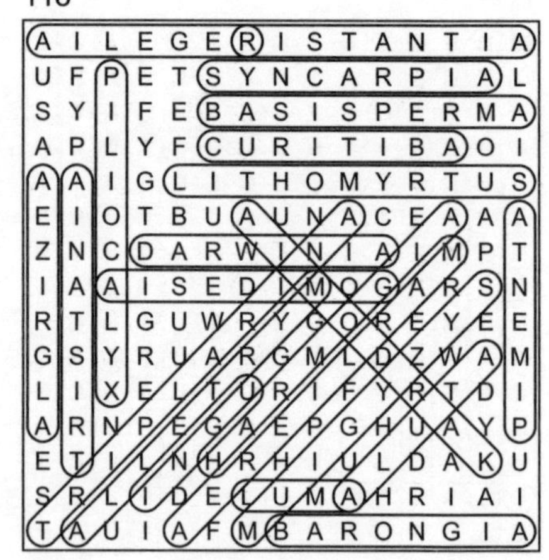

119

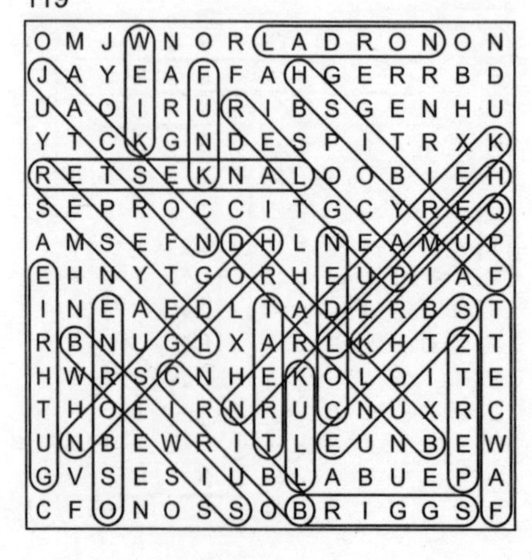

120

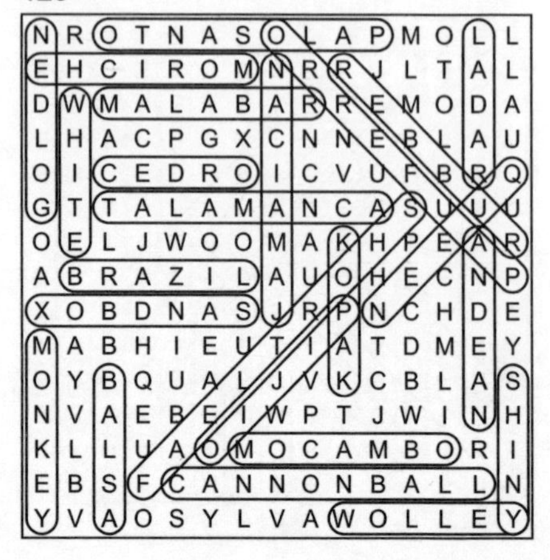

Solutions

121

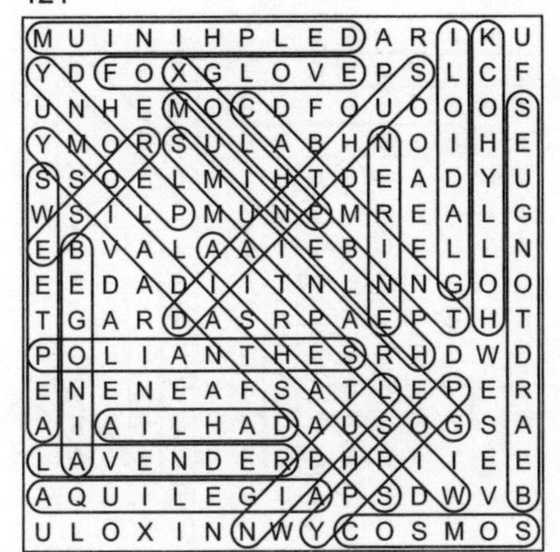

122

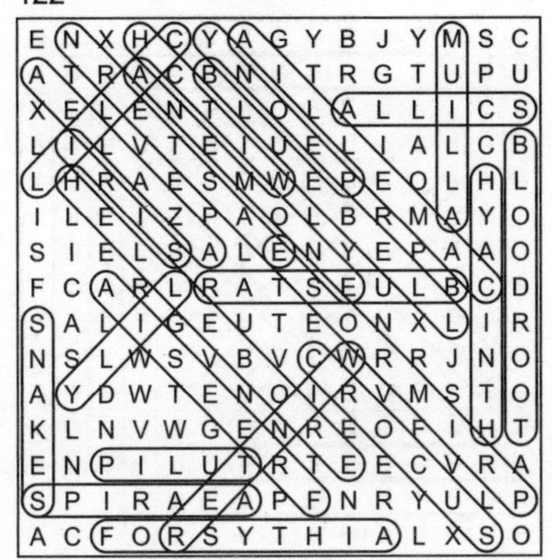

123

124

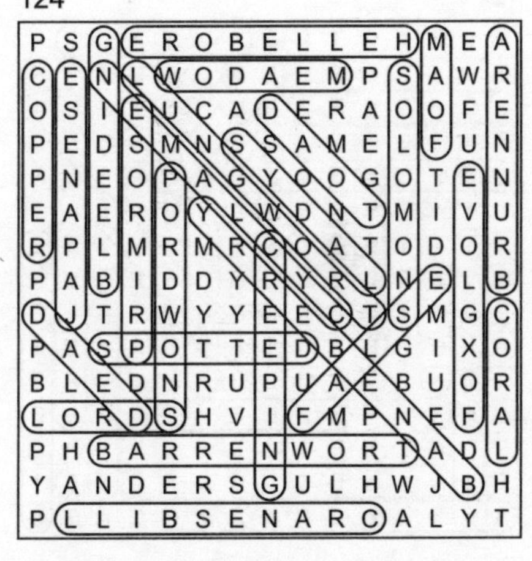

125

126

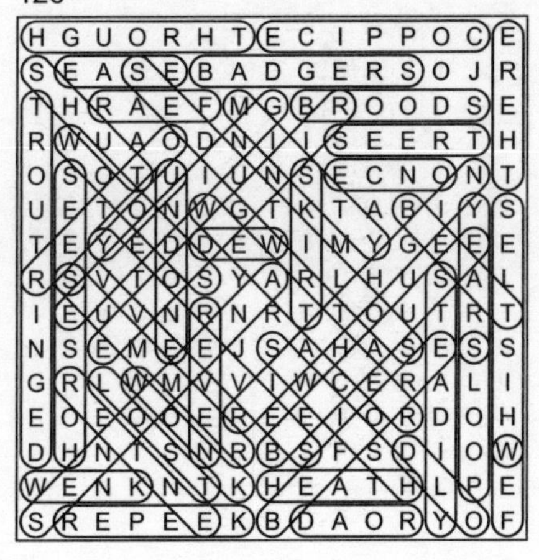

Solutions

127

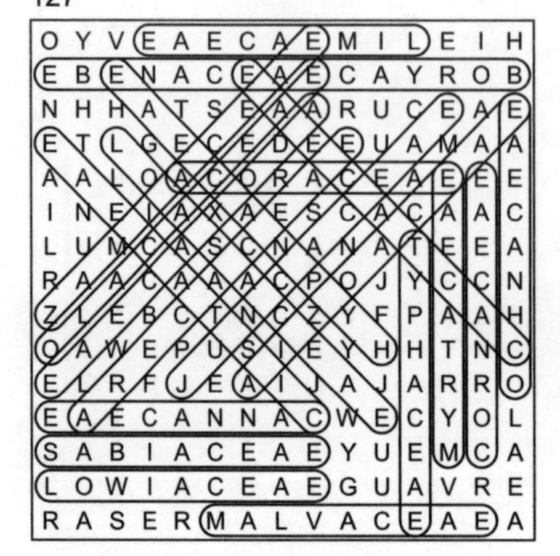

128

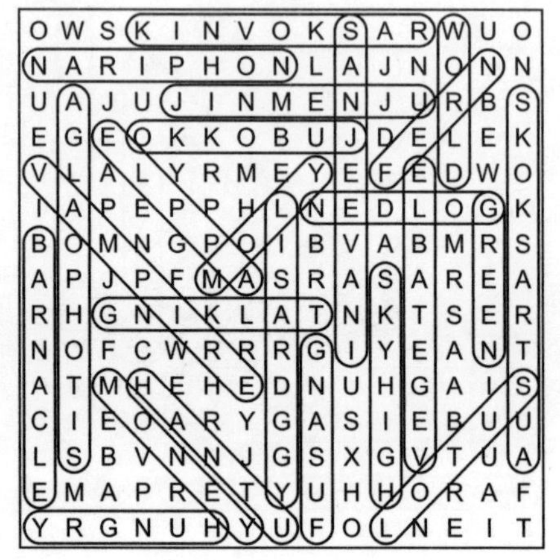

129